LIVING WITH MENTAL ILLNESS

Reports of
The Institute of Community Studies

LIVING WITH
MENTAL ILLNESS

A Study in East London

Enid Mills

Foreword by
Morris Carstairs

LONDON
ROUTLEDGE & KEGAN PAUL

First published 1962
by Routledge & Kegan Paul Limited
Broadway House, 68–74 Carter Lane
London, E.C.4

Printed in Great Britain
by W. & J. Mackay & Co. Ltd., Chatham

© *Institute of Community Studies* 1962

CONTENTS

TABLES

FOREWORD

DURING the past few years there have been great changes in the treatment of the mentally ill, changes as revolutionary as those introduced at the turn of the eighteenth century by Tuke and Pinel, the pioneers of modern psychiatric practice. These changes have been attended by a spirit of therapeutic optimism, albeit a guarded optimism: no one is confident of being able to *cure* the victims of serious mental illness, but we do at least have remedies which will alleviate their distress.

The emphasis is now laid on early treatment, on social rehabilitation, and particularly on rescuing patients from the fate of being secluded for long periods in large, remote mental hospitals. 'Community care' is the current slogan. Some authorities (including the present Minister of Health) have argued that if more trouble is taken to treat psychiatric patients in their homes, or in general hospitals near their homes, the need for large mental hospitals may soon become much less. Already the numbers of patients resident in these hospitals has begun to decline, although their annual admission rates have risen steeply year by year.

The frequency of serious mental illness has not declined, but more mental patients are remaining among us in the community instead of being shut away. We see here another facet of social change: our society is coming to accept responsibility for helping its mentally affected members, as in the past it has learned to relieve gross poverty and physical ill-health. Not only the insane but also criminals, another class once totally rejected by society, are now being offered opportunities of re-adapting themselves to an acceptable role in the community.

This is a major change of social policy. Mad people are not easy to live with; it is much simpler for their neighbours to put them under lock and key. If we are going to be more generous in recognizing the patients' claims, we must be prepared to put up with some inconvenience on their behalf. How much inconvenience the public can tolerate, the next few years will show.

At this turning point in the social provision for the insane it is valuable to be confronted with a study such as Enid Mills has done. Here we have a picture of what actually happened to people who became mentally ill in an East London borough in 1956 and 1957. She tells us who these people were, and where they lived, to whom they and their relatives turned for help. She describes the concrete events which accompany mental illness, the attitudes and reactions of the patients' kinsfolk and their neighbours, and the part played by various institutions and social agencies. Of these, the most important is Long Grove, a mental hospital in Epsom, 25 miles away, to which has been assigned the task of admitting mental patients from the borough.

Miss Mills takes pains to point out the limitations of her data in numbers, time and place. She has deliberately confined her attention to patients from one area because this enables her to profit by the earlier investigations in East London of the Institute of Community Studies.

Some of the facts of our mental health services are so peculiar that it is difficult at times to remember that the incidents reported here are not episodes in past history, but happened only the other day; in spite of the humane intervention of the Mental Health Act (1959) this is still largely the picture of mental illness and its treatment in our big cities today. The Act has opened up new possibilities, by simplifying the legal side of mental treatment, and by encouraging local authorities to provide the means for efficient community care. Enid Mills concludes her survey with a discussion of community mental health services, followed by a review of the difficulties which must be overcome if the transition is to be effected from an outmoded, remote mental hospital system to a community-based service which will be at once efficient and humane.

MORRIS CARSTAIRS

ACKNOWLEDGEMENTS

THIS study was made possible by grants to the Institute of Community Studies from the Mental Health Research Fund and in its later stages from the Joseph Rowntree Memorial Trust; I am grateful to both these bodies for their support. The report owes much to the help and supervision of my colleague Peter Marris to whom I should like to extend my especial thanks for his co-operation and interest. I should also like to thank my colleagues Michael Young, Peter Willmott, Howard Dickinson, Ralph Samuel, Phyllis Willmott, Mary Barclay and Ann Cartwright for their help and advice. I am indebted to Daphne Chandler, Polly Kasserer, Pat Lovelock, Helen Linge and Anne Shelver for typing interviews and manuscripts.

The members of the Advisory Committee kindly read the drafts of the report and advised upon them. I am particularly grateful to Professor G. M. Carstairs and to Robin Huws Jones for the help they have given during the preparation of the report.

Dennis Marsden and Dr. Peter Hey shared the task of completing the interviews with me and I would like to thank them for the friendly co-operation which they both gave in circumstances which were often very difficult. Marjorie Durbin kindly collected data from the hospital. For advice and information concerning statistical material I would like to convey my thanks to Miss E. M. Brooke and Wolf Scott. My thanks are also due to Professor J. Morris and Dr. R. Tredgold who kindly arranged for me to attend discussion groups and seminars at the London Hospital and University College Hospital, while Dr. E. W. Dunkley allowed me to visit St. Pancras Hospital Observation Unit on a number of occasions and I am deeply grateful to him for his personal interest in the survey and his continual advice.

Dr. Ernest Gruenberg of the Milbank Memorial Fund, New York, Dr. Douglas Bennett of the Netherne Hospital and Dr. John Clausen of the National Institute of Mental Health, Bethesda, U.S.A., have all been most generous in giving help and commenting on the report, while fellow sociologists in the mental health field, George Brown and Stephen Folkard, have also helped with information on many occasions.

I should like to thank the staff of the Ministry of Labour and that of the London County Council Public Health, Housing and Welfare departments for their co-operation and also the local borough council, the settlements, missions, doctors, vicars, the Citizens' Advice Bureau, the Legal Advice Bureau, the Family Service Units, Family Welfare Association and the many public servants who assisted in my inquiry into community services. To the National Assistance Board I would like to express my especial thanks for the courtesy and consideration with which access to a wide range of officers was made possible, and to the Ministry of Pensions and National Insurance, who supplied detailed replies to queries concerning patients' earnings, insurance, sickness benefits and pension rights.

I should also like to express my appreciation to Dr. A. B. Monro, Physician Superintendent of Long Grove Hospital, for his permission to visit the hospital whenever necessary; to Dr. John Denham, Consultant Psychiatrist, for his interest and help; and to the many other members of the hospital staff for their friendly co-operation.

Finally, I wish to thank the patients and relatives who took part in this survey for their unstinted help, their frequent humour and their unfailing goodwill.

I

INTRODUCTION

THE importance of mental illness is now well recognized. About half the hospital beds in this country are occupied by the mentally sick. The Registrar General[1] points out that 'There has been a striking increase in the numbers of both first and total admissions to mental hospitals and in the numbers of departures and discharges. . . . First admissions in 1956 exceeded those for 1951 by 23% for males and 22% for females; the numbers who were admitted for a second or subsequent visit meanwhile increased by 75 and 79% respectively. Discharges and departures increased by 54 and 58% for males and females. . . . There has therefore been a very much more rapid turnover of patients in recent years, without a corresponding increase in the number of resident patients.' There were nearly 150,000 mental patients in hospital at the end of 1956.

Some further indication of the extent of mental illness in the population at large can be gathered from a survey of General Practices undertaken in 1955 and 1956.[2] In the period May 1955 to April 1956, a survey was made of 106 practices in England and Wales. In every 1,000 patients consulting their G.P., 50 were subsequently diagnosed as suffering from a mental, psychoneurotic or personality disorder and they consulted the doctor on average 3·7 times a year. That is roughly 5% of all consultations.

Mental illness is clearly an urgent problem. This was recognized by the appointment in 1954 of a Royal Com-

[1] *Supplement on Mental Health, Statistical Review of England and Wales 1954-56.*
[2] Logan, W. P. D., and Cushion, A. A., *Morbidity Statistics from General Practice.*

mission, whose conclusions were published in May 1957.[1] The main recommendations were that there should be a movement away from legal certification towards informal admission to mental hospitals and that long confinement in hospital should be replaced by better care in the community. But what does care in the community mean? What does it mean to be a psychotic living in our society, or his relative? These are questions on which it is hoped to throw a little light.

The nature of the problem

The following paragraph is quoted from a letter written by the relative of a middle-aged unmarried man, previously a psychotic patient, who returned home from a mental hospital after 20 years.

'How does it affect us—can one explain what is happening? All that we know is that we manage to live with it. To care for somebody with a sick body is one thing. At least you can reach him, understand him, and he will make certain responses that will help us carry on. But with a sick mind we must shoulder an extra burden. We must think for the person and get little response; talk to them and get unencouraging answers. It is a battle of wits which one can never win. We feel frustrated by the fact that here is a person—maybe physically fit, yet unable to muster an iota of strength, with thoughts radiating things to him which to him are real—thoughts which we are powerless to counteract as we cannot get on the same wavelength. Who is the patient to turn to? Who is to befriend him in his months of rehabilitation? Must he go alone for the rest of time?'

As both the admissions and discharges from mental hospitals are increasing, more and more families will experience the same problem of adjustment when a mental patient returns home often still in need of treatment. But

---

[1] *Report of the Royal Commission on the Law Relating to Mental Illness and Mental Deficiency.*

we know too little of the family background of the mentally ill and the problems of caring for them at home. The more we hope to turn mental hospitals from asylums for incurables into places of treatment, the more we shall need to return the mentally sick to their own homes to complete their rehabilitation. To what homes will they return? What kind of homes do they come from? Have they anyone to care for them? Where do practical and emotional difficulties arise? How do they and their families think of the illness and the kind of treatment they need? Can we provide treatment for them at home in a way they will accept? In this book I have tried to show how these questions affected a group of patients from an East London borough, admitted to hospital in 1956 and 1957 and studied in 1958 and 1959. Since only a small-scale study was possible it seemed best to concentrate upon one community. This area was chosen because previous work by the Institute of Community Studies had already established many of the characteristics of ordinary family life in the district.

The survey

The patients who co-operated in this survey were selected from the admission register of Long Grove Hospital, Epsom. The admissions to Long Grove, which has an East London catchment area, follow the trends discernible in the national figures in the main, though with certain individual variations. The total admissions to Long Grove Hospital rose from 884 in 1954 to 1,382 in 1959. During the two years covered by this study (1956 and 1957) the admissions were 1,031 and 1,537 respectively. The average admission from the survey borough is 64 per year.

This hospital receives most of the patients from the borough. The Registrar General's records show that only about 7% of patients from this area are admitted elsewhere, and they are distributed among six hospitals. To obtain a sample for the survey the names of all patients from the borough surveyed, who were admitted to Long Grove between January 1956 and December 1957, were taken from the register, together with those of their next of kin. There were 120 patients, of whom it was possible to trace 89.[1] As far as possible, both the patient and his relative were interviewed, but sometimes one or other could not be traced, or would ask the interviewer not to contact the other. Altogether, 76 patients and 74 relatives were interviewed in 1958 and 1959, and information was obtained from either the patient or his family for 86. Three refused. The experiences of these 86 patients, and the provision made for them by the community, are the subject of this book.

If the patient was still in hospital, or lived alone after his discharge, his relative (whose name had been recorded on the admission register) was usually approached first. If he lived with relatives, the interviewing began with the first to be contacted—usually whoever opened the door and let the interviewer in. Wherever possible, arrangements were made to talk to the patient and a relative separately. Twenty-four patients and 50 relatives were interviewed alone at home, 32 patients and 24 relatives together with others in their home. The remaining 20 patients were interviewed while they were still in hospital.

The families were first contacted by the interviewer calling on them at home. Even a letter of introduction from the hospital, which the interviewer carried, turned out to be more confusing than reassuring. The best introduction proved to be a verbal explanation on the doorstep. As one patient said, 'Come on in, I can *see* you're not going to eat me.'

The interview

The schedule itself was in three parts.[2] In the first were recorded the members of the patient's household, both at the time of the interview and before his last admission; the amenities of the house; his birthplace and length of resi-

[1] For information concerning the remainder see Appendix 2.
[2] A copy of the interview schedule is reproduced in Appendix 1.

dence in the borough; his education, occupation, and means of livelihood; the number of times he had been admitted to hospital. The second part dealt with the patient's own account of his illness—how he came to be admitted to hospital, what he felt about his treatment, and how he saw his difficulties. To this was attached a chart of his parents, children, brothers and sisters, noting where they lived, how often he saw them, whether they visited him in hospital; also included were other relatives with whom he mentioned a particularly close tie. In the third part, the relative closest to the patient was asked to describe, from his own point of view, the onset of the illness, his relationship with the doctor and the hospital, his own attitude towards the patient's illness and its treatment, and any difficulties he had encountered in caring for the patient at home. Each complete schedule was made up of two interviews, lasting from 20 minutes, at the least, to three hours. In spite of their illness, only 14 patients were difficult to interview coherently, and such discrepancies as appeared between the information given in the two interviews could usually be clarified without difficulty. Where necessary, a second visit was paid, and several of the patients continued to keep in touch with the interviewer, either calling at the office, or meeting her in the street or the parks where those who are not working sometimes pass part of their day.

The patients ranged in age from 19 to over 80, almost half of them being between 30 and 59, the remainder equally divided between the young and old. There were 40 men and 46 women. Half the men were married, all but two of the remainder being single, while the women were more evenly distributed between the married, single and widowed and divorced. Single women, however, predominated.

How do the patients compare with the population of the survey borough in age and sex?

As Table I shows, the sexes are equally represented among patients and among non-patients. In both cases women accounted for 54% of the total.

TABLE I

SEX AND AGE OF PATIENTS, COMPARED WITH POPULATION OF
SURVEY BOROUGH

		Patients *1956–57*		*Population of Survey Borough* *aged 15 and over (Census 1951)*
MEN				
15–34 ..	.. 16	40%		40%
35–64 ..	.. 17	43%		48%
65 or over	.. 17	17%		12%
Total	.. 40	100%		100%
		— —		(21,438)
Men as % of total				
population ..		46%		46%
WOMEN				
15–34 ..	.. 12	26%		38%
35–64 ..	.. 24	52%		47%
65 or over	.. 10	22%		15%
Total	.. 46	100%		100%
		— —		(24,538)
Women as % of				
total population		54%		54%

For both men and women, patients include a higher proportion of old people, aged 65 or over.[1] The men have a
correspondingly lower proportion in the middle group
(aged 35–64); women in the younger group (aged 15–34).

Twenty-seven of the patients had been diagnosed as
schizophrenic, 21 as depressive, and 13 as suffering from
diseases of old age: a classification of the patients under
15 diagnostic labels is given in Appendix 2. Although the
nature of the illness must influence behaviour, and so the

[1] The tendency for admission rates to rise with age is discussed in Appendix 2.

social situation of the patient, this study is concerned more with the social problems common to all mental patients than with their differences. These differences of diagnosis have therefore been ignored for the most part in the discussion.

The report

This book is divided into two parts. Part One discusses the attitudes towards mental illness and its treatment expressed in these interviews, and the experience of admission to hospital as the patients and their families related it. The second chapter describes how these 86 men and women came to enter Long Grove Hospital. The study must begin here, for it is by their admission to hospital[1] that they are publicly identified as mentally ill.

In the third chapter the patients' length of stay and experiences in hospital are discussed, while the fourth explores the perception of mental illness and its relation to patterns of residence in hospital.

Chapter V examines the attitudes of the patients to the hospital,[2] which are directly related to their interpretation of mental illness. Chapters VI and VII discuss the family and home environment. The structure of the family and the neighbourhood and the position held in both by the mentally sick person may be crucial in deciding admission to hospital or retention in the community. Part Two of the book is about the community services. The information it contains is based on a series of informal interviews. The final chapter discusses some of the implications for policy.

Since the study was designed to explore the role of the mentally ill in their family and community, and was deliberately restricted to one borough where some information, both quantitative and qualitative, was available about normal patterns of family life, it cannot offer any general conclusions. The numbers are too few for any very refined

---

[1] The majority of patients admitted from this area have not attended as psychiatric out-patients prior to their first admission to mental hospital.
[2] For the historical development of these attitudes see Appendix 3.

statistical analysis to be fruitful, and the borough is certainly not wholly typical, even of East London. The purpose of the book is rather to suggest the kind of associations between admission to hospital and social circumstances which appear, on this limited evidence, to be probable, in the hope that research workers and psychiatrists will find them worth pursuing. In part, too, the aim is simply to describe the experience of mental illness from the point of view of the patient and his family and to offer some suggestions about the way in which community care might be made more effective. Though the problem of treatment and of attitudes to mental illness have often been investigated from the point of view of the medical profession and society at large, we seldom look at them as they are seen by those most intimately and painfully concerned.

The reader is asked to bear in mind that this survey was started in 1958. Since then public policy on mental health has changed more than at any time in the last 50 years, and Long Grove Hospital itself has changed a great deal. Most of the wards are now open. The building has been altered and pleasantly redecorated. More than 100 patients go out to work from the hospital and several types of industrial work have been introduced into it as well. The number of social workers has doubled. Patients' clubs with parallel organizations in the home area have been formed and visits are exchanged. The patient-staff ratio has improved. More patients go home on leave. Some wards are now mixed. Prejudices are slowly beginning to recede in the districts from which people go to Long Grove, as more young patients, who entered hospital acutely ill, return home cured, or very much improved.

Under the Mental Health Act of 1959 much can be done to improve communications and relations between the hospital and the local community it serves. Many problems still remain to be solved. The improvements in the hospital are unevenly distributed. But it is now true to say that, in some parts of the hospital, today's problem is to prevent patients from becoming too happily settled in comfortable surroundings with congenial companions and thus to handicap them in facing the harsher realities outside hospital. In some important ways, therefore, the picture presented in the following pages is already out of date. Yet the impression, from talking to people in the borough since the research was completed, is that local feeling is still hostile to the hospital, and that mental patients still face many of the problems described in Part One of this book.

PART ONE
The Experience of
Mental Illness

II

BECOMING A PATIENT

MRS. SWALLOW[1] smoothed a pair of socks on to her husband's feet and helped him into his shirt and trousers. His doctor, whom Mr. Swallow knew well, had offered to take him for a drive in the country, and mentioned that Mr. Swallow's son Henry was coming too. Richard Swallow accepted the invitation eagerly. He entered the ambulance quite happily; it was only when they entered the mental hospital that he began to offer violent objections. On returning home his son Henry sat down and wept, telling his mother, 'When Dad realized where he was, he called me every name he could think of. I ought never to have gone.'

Richard Swallow is one of 120 men and women from this borough who entered Long Grove Hospital in 1956 and 1957. As he entered the gates of the hospital he became, for the first time, a mental patient—someone whose behaviour, in the eyes of society, is not merely strange, but diseased. It is a hard truth to accept, of yourself, or of someone you love. For to call someone mentally ill is to put in question his competence in every social relationship. Once he is admitted to hospital, his behaviour receives an interpretation from which no amount of protest can extricate him, since little he may say or do will be accepted at its face value. He is no longer regarded as his own master, but as mastered by the sickness of his mind.

Few people, therefore, dare acknowledge that they are

---

[1] Names given to patients and relatives throughout this report are fictitious and identities disguised.

mentally ill. Most will search for other explanations of their difficulties, and other ways of solving them. To enter a mental hospital is an admission that they have failed, and whatever the circumstances which led to it, the event is crucial to their relationship with the society in which they live. They acquire a new status, in which, though they gain hope of a cure, they may lose the right to be considered responsible for their own affairs. They are recognized as a special group within society.

In 1956 and 1957, entry to the hospital could be achieved in any one of the four ways formally laid down in the Lunacy Act, 1890, or by a fifth and sixth method under the Mental Treatment Act 1930.[1]

1. *Reception Order on Petition*

The next of kin, or a non-relative empowered to act, petitioned for the reception of the sick person into a recognized mental hospital or licensed house.[2] The petition was supported by two separate medical certificates, one of which was issued by the patient's usual doctor. A third document gave factual details about the patient, and the course of his illness. If the petition succeeded the reception order issued was signed by an appropriate judicial authority.

2. *Summary Reception Order*

No written petition was required, but a statement had to be signed by the Mental Welfare Officer (who must be 'duly authorized' and therefore became known as the D.A.O.). The patient was also seen by a doctor and a J.P. Relatives or non-relatives could summon the D.A.O. In the case of a person entering hospital as a private patient two medical certificates were required.

3. *Urgency Order*

In emergencies, a doctor who had just seen the patient could summon the D.A.O., who came as soon as possible

---

[1] For alterations brought about by the Mental Health Act 1959 see Appendix 3.
[2] A place licensed by the Minister of Health for receiving mental patients.

and removed the patient directly to a mental hospital. Admission to the hospital had to take place within two clear days of the order, and a statement of the particulars made by the D.A.O., with one medical certificate, attached. The signature of the nearest relative available who had seen the patient within the last two days was obtained. The urgency order remained in force for seven days, by which time the patient was discharged, certified, or accepted as a voluntary patient.

4. *Inquisition*

This was mainly used where the sick person owned a large estate and complicated legal procedures were used to protect the property. A judge, or judge and jury held an inquiry into whether a person so alleged was of unsound mind and incapable of managing his own affairs.

5. *Voluntary Admission*

Under the Mental Treatment Act of 1930, any person wishing to receive treatment could sign an application to the person in charge of a hospital or licensed house 'to be received as a voluntary patient in an institution within the meaning of the Act, or in any hospital, nursing home or place approved for the purpose by the Board of Control,[1] or into the charge, as a single patient, of a person so approved'. Voluntary patients were required to give three days' notice in writing if they left otherwise than discharged by the hospital. The hospital was required to notify the Board of Control of the reception, death or departure of voluntary patients.

If the Board of Control considered the person unfit to be a voluntary patient the Superintendent was asked to discharge the patient, or treat him as a 'person of unsound mind' or as a person in need of temporary treatment.

The Board of Control was set up to protect the legal rights (other than property rights which are governed by the Court of Protection) of mental patients, and to inspect and supervise mental hospitals. For further details see Appendix 3.

6. *The Temporary Treatment* of non-volitional patients without
certification became possible under the 1930 Act. Application was made by a spouse or relative supported by a re-
commendation signed by two doctors, one of whom, if
possible, was the patient's usual G.P., and the other a
doctor approved for this purpose by the Minister of Health.
Action had to be taken within 14 days of the medical
examination. Temporary patients were detained for six
months unless they recovered completely, or sufficiently
to refuse treatment, after which they were detained for 28
days. If necessary they could be held for further periods,
not to exceed six months in all.

The patients coming to Long Grove in 1956 or 1957
could enter as voluntary or temporary patients under the
1930 Act, or as certified patients governed by the 1890 Act,
their general welfare ultimately supervised by the Board of
Control, which was soon to be abolished under the 1959
Act, or, by the end of 1957, as non-statutory patients in
some 'de-designated' part of the hospital. The non-statutory
patients could enter and leave without formality of any
kind, and this paved the way for the informal admission
system introduced by the 1959 Act.

These, then, were the formal regulations in force at the
time when the patients in this study were in hospital. The
men and women in the sample—86 of the 120 who were
admitted to Long Grove Hospital in 1956 and 1957—were
admitted under the regulations described above in sections
two, three, and five. But a mere statement of the legal
machinery gives a misleadingly incomplete picture of how
these people became patients. Reality is untidy and the law
precise. Since the circumstances which led up to admission
were so diverse the regulations could seldom be followed
to the letter. Doctors, D.A.O.s and relatives had to adapt
procedure as best they could, within the limits of the law.
Usually what actually happened was edited and reinter-
preted to fit the available legal categories. These official
labels are therefore classificatory rather than descriptive,

and it is necessary to look beyond them to understand how patients are in practice admitted.

Thus, although 55 of the men and women in this study were classified as voluntary patients, the majority of them did not actively seek treatment of their own free will. 'Voluntary' meant not legally certifiable, and able to leave hospital after giving notice in writing, rather than choosing to receive treatment and taking steps to obtain it. Only 12 freely and deliberately sought admission for themselves. Some of those 12 found it easier to accept that they were mentally ill because the illness was associated with physical symptoms for which they had sought treatment.

Voluntary patients

Ralph Jackson, for instance, became moody and over-anxious because of the shock of his illness, which left him partially handicapped. After meeting a relative by marriage, who had recently returned from a mental hospital, and greatly impressed by the change in her appearance, he applied via the out-patients clinic for admission to Long Grove. Mr. Horton, on the other hand, had a sudden attack of a frightening illness and when told by the general hospital that it was entirely psychological in origin, he insisted on immediate admission to Long Grove Hospital. Similarly, Paul Golinsky accepted the offer of treatment because, added to his mental disturbance, he suffered from a particular neurological disorder and was willing to be a guinea-pig in the hope that he might be cured of at least one misfortune. He said earnestly, 'If it would have helped I'd have let them take my head off and put it on again. I went to the hospital so they could do something for it.'

But physical symptoms will not lead people to accept psychiatric help unless they can see the mental hospital as relevant to their needs. This is easier, perhaps, for the younger people, who think of Long Grove as a hospital rather than an 'Asylum'—the word still carved beside its door. Vincent Murdoch insisted on seeking treatment, in spite of a discouraging beginning. He was discharged from the Army on medical grounds. 'I went sick and when I saw the Board the officer said, "Don't be a fool. Snap out of it. You'll have to go and see a nut specialist and then there'll be a lot of trouble." You don't expect them to say a thing like that to somebody, but that's the way in the Army.' Almost as soon as he had been discharged, he made an appointment to see a psychiatrist. 'The specialist asked me if I'd like to go away and I thought it would be a good idea. It looked nice on the brochures that he showed me. There was all contemporary furnishings and decorations and the grounds were laid out very well. I thought it would be a sort of convalescent home.' So Vincent Murdoch signed the form asking for admission as a voluntary patient, and when he had received a letter from the hospital he packed his suitcase and travelled down to Epsom on the train. After inquiry at the lodge at the hospital gates, he made his way to the main building and was met by a nurse.

For these four people admission was the result of deliberate choice. The eight other patients who came of their own choice were not quite so capable of seeing themselves into hospital—some came by ambulance and others asked a relative to accompany them—but, like these four, it was their decision to enter hospital.

There were also 15 who were eventually persuaded to enter hospital, though with reluctance, and sometimes under pressure. Nine of them had been receiving treatment for physical illness and were advised by their doctors to enter a mental hospital—though the words 'mental hospital' were rarely, if ever, mentioned. Mr. Atterbury, for instance, had suffered a very severe accident and a series of operations, and finally, as he put it, his 'nerves went to pieces'. He was led to believe that he was going to a convalescent home[1] in the country for a rest and a chance for his nerves to recover. When he came in sight of the hospital gates he began to wonder what sort of place he had come to. At the

This statement was made by five patients with reference to the same doctor.

front door he noticed the word 'Asylum' carved in the stone and began to feel frightened. He complained bitterly that he had been 'swindled' into a mental hospital.

Sometimes persuasion amounted almost to threats. Mr. Higgs also suffered from shock after injury in an air-raid, and developed the habit of reliving the incident in his sleep and waking in a state of great terror. Finally he attempted to commit suicide and the doctor told his relatives that unless Henry Higgs agreed to accept treatment, he would have to take the matter further. Henry was cajoled into signing as a voluntary patient by his sister. But more often, the doctors were able to persuade their patients without either trickery or threats.

The others who became voluntary patients at Long Grove had not been consulted before their admission. Fourteen went there on the initiative of their relatives. Their parents, children, brothers or sisters, their wives or even occasionally more distant relatives—a brother-in-law, grandmother or aunt—arranged for them to enter hospital, and they themselves signed the form asking for admission only after they had arrived at an observation unit or the hospital itself. In six instances the relatives' decision was the result of a long series of incidents; in the remaining eight the request for admission came as the result of a sudden and sometimes violent crisis. One patient threw off her clothes and ran out naked in the middle of a bitter winter night, another quarrelled with his son and hit him violently, a young patient smashed the contents of his room and then refused to eat or speak for a week. The violence among this group often exceeds that of the patients who were certified. Other patients were not at all violent, but the family came to the conclusion that treatment was needed. The patient signed the forms unaware of what was happening[1] and too distracted for the relatives to reason with him. As Mrs. Kerstein explained 'They wanted to certify him one time, when he didn't know what he was doing and wouldn't sign

[1] E.g. 'He thought it was his pension form.'

19

the form, but I said I'd get him to sign it and I did—I told him it was something else.'

There is often painful conflict in the family over such decisions. Mrs. Fryers had been ill for almost two years, in a complete state of misery, reducing her family to despair. Her daughter said, 'We honestly prayed she would die rather than go on like that.' As a last resort the children decided the mother should go to Long Grove. Her husband did nothing to prevent this, but accepted it as defeat. 'When the ambulance came for Mum he shut himself in his room, he couldn't stand it, he thought she'd be locked up and die in there and he'd never see her at home any more.'

Sometimes the relatives arrived at their decision only slowly and painfully after years of strain. Mrs. Brown had nursed her husband at home for more than 12 years. Eventually he became quite helpless and incontinent. The facilities for washing were very limited and even with help from the Red Cross she still found it necessary to dry sheets round the fire almost continuously during the winter. At the same time she cared for an invalid child. When the child became bed-ridden for a while, Mrs. Brown came near to collapse and the doctor persuaded her to think about letting her husband go into hospital. The doctor asked the council welfare officer to call and discuss the matter with Mrs. Brown. Some days later, without warning of any kind, an ambulance arrived to collect the patient and convey him to hospital. Mrs. Brown insisted on accompanying her husband in the ambulance in spite of the nurse's attempt to dissuade her. On arrival at Long Grove she said that she would not leave until she had seen him in bed in the ward in which he had been placed. 'The nurse on duty was very friendly,' she said. 'When I told him my husband was dying of thirst he said to me, "Don't worry, girl, I'll fix him a cup of tea in a jiffy, we've got tea on the go all day here"—I thought it was a bit familiar like, but he was very kind and friendly to my husband.' In this case the decision to agree to admission to Long Grove had taken almost 15 years.

Fourteen became 'voluntary patients' only under considerable pressure. Five came directly through the Law Courts. They were put on probation on condition that they accepted treatment in a mental hospital, and all of them considered admission to hospital as something in lieu of a prison sentence. One of these patients gave a policeman a black eye when he spoke to her and another was found drunk and violent in the street, one was taken to court for petty thieving, one was found wandering and disturbing the peace and the fifth attempted to drive cars away to reach the lady for whom he had developed a passion—as he had never driven a car in his life the results attracted the attention of the police. Three others were taken to a general hospital after attempted suicide and were offered the choice of Long Grove or the police station.

The remaining six of these voluntary patients reached hospital through the intervention of a health visitor, a neighbour, or a general hospital. Three complained that they had been kidnapped.

Though they resented the way in which they had been brought to hospital, many of these voluntary patients finally accepted treatment, and were afterwards grateful for it. But it remains true that out of 55, only 12 had really sought treatment, while 28 had only been brought to accept it by deception or threats. There remain 31 who were certified.

Certified patients

In general, people are certified either to protect others, or for their own protection because they are no longer able to care for themselves. Amongst the latter are many elderly senile people who were either living alone or with inadequate care. Mrs. Seymour and Miss Pravdin both came from Russian immigrant families. Now with few relatives, weak and ailing, they find themselves in a mental hospital. Their lives have been full of tragedy, poverty and upheaval ever since they were born. They were both interviewed in hospital and each of them begged to return to their own homes.

Both Mrs. Seymour and Miss Pravdin lived in basement flats with very difficult stone steps leading up to street level. Mrs. Seymour is partially paralysed and Miss Pravdin unable to walk far. Miss Pravdin lived alone and after a series of bad falls and accidents it was decided that she was too confused to care for herself any longer. She has only one close relative whom she had not seen for many years. When the relative was traced he was neither willing nor able to care for her and she was therefore certified.

Approximately one-third of the certified patients were senile, and there were two other main groups. Slightly less than a third were certified because of very sudden and very violent outbursts, and the remainder at the end of a series of incidents which became less and less tolerable to others.

Mr. Frank Texter, for example, had shown no signs of disturbance until the night on which he suddenly attacked his wife and attempted to murder his little daughter. After this he went berserk and was carried into the ambulance only with the help of three men. His wife had to run for help, taking the children with her and leaving her husband locked in the home. His behaviour was particularly unexpected as he is normally a very gentle man and particularly devoted to his children. His wife, terrified for her children, accepted the fact that he would be certified without the slightest objection.

Not all the certified patients were violent. A number of them were just a source of constant irritation to their neighbours. Miss Guarita was certified because the neighbours could no longer stand her screams, while Mrs. Chidley developed paranoid delusions about her neighbours, which led to a court case and thus to her certification. A series of incidents ending in a burglary[1] led her to believe that her neighbours had designs on her husband, her pro-

---

[1] It is an odd but interesting fact that five of the paranoic patients broke down and went to hospital after a burglary as if this event triggered off feelings which were close to the surface but dormant. See Appendix 3 for further discussion in relation to Listwan, I., 'Mental Disorders in Migrants'.

perty and herself; as a result of these beliefs she not only took various bizarre precautions against burglars and the neighbours, but abused the people living near by in extremely violent language. After several complaints to Mr. Chidley, the neighbours took the matter to court and Mr. Chidley had to promise that he would arrange for his wife to have treatment. As he described it, 'Two men came to the house and she talked to them and showed them what she had ready for the burglars and everything. They said she'd have to go away. One morning when I was at work I said to my boy that works with me, "I have a feeling that everything is not right at home. I'll just go up and see." I was just in time to see them putting my wife in the ambulance, and my daughter crying her eyes out. They didn't send us no warning or anything.'

The ambulance called for Miss Paul at breakfast. She too had been quarrelling with the neighbours and as this was in council property, where she lived alone, a welfare officer arranged for her to be taken to hospital where she was considered to be certifiable and was transferred to Long Grove Hospital. She described what happened. 'I'd just put my head outside my front door to fetch the milk in—when they knocked I thought it was the milk and I wanted my breakfast. If I'd have known what it was I'd never have opened the door that morning. They grabbed hold of me, those ambulance men, and dragged me, all frightened and crying, down the stairs to the ambulance—and that slut from next door shouting after me, "I told you I'd have you put away" and swearing at me.' Miss Paul's only relative, a sister who lived near by, received a letter from the hospital two days after her sister was certified.

Mr. Swallow is one of the few certified patients who were 'put away' by the family and who recovered and returned home with everything cheerfully forgiven and forgotten. Even the hallucinations which led his wife to give up in despair were, like the man himself, cheerful and appealing. His wife said, 'He began wandering the streets a bit, then

23

I'd come home from my part-time job and find he'd left the door wide open. Then I found he'd taken things out of the wardrobe and given them away. One time I found him outside the house giving our things to the people in the street going by and telling the crowd he'd been made a millionaire. What he was and what he wasn't going to do for them! First thing he was going to have all lovely houses built for them. Then he was going to give all the old-age pensioners as much money as they liked.' Finally, when Mr. Swallow had disappeared on one or two occasions, his wife agreed with the doctor and Mr. Swallow was invited to 'go for a ride in the country'.

However we may wish that treatment in a mental hospital should be accepted as rationally and dispassionately as any other medical service, these illustrations suggest how seldom this is so. The illness itself is only one factor in the confused and often fortuitous circumstances which surround the admission of a mental patient.

On the one hand there is the problem of the perception of behaviour as mentally disturbed (and, as later chapters will show, the definitions and interpretations of mental illness are extremely diverse), and on the other the double difficulty of making an appropriate decision and knowing how to put it into effect. Should these difficulties be overcome, there can still be considerable variety in patients' experience of getting to hospital.

Duly Authorized Officer

If, for example, the Duly Authorized Officer has been summoned to the East London area, the patient may be taken by ambulance direct to Long Grove Hospital, or to any one of six psychiatric observation units at Dulwich, Bow, Battersea, Fulham, St. Pancras or Tooting. While in theory the patient will be taken to the observation unit nearest his home, and in theory there should be 224 beds available to the D.A.O.s in London, in practice there are approximately 160. A patient may have to be admitted to an observation unit where it is inconvenient for his relatives to visit him. Officially a patient admitted to an observation unit on an Order remains only 17 days, so that visiting problems should not be prolonged. But some patients are then classified as informal or voluntary patients and may sometimes remain as long as three months for treatment, instead of being transferred to a mental hospital, while others may be transferred within a few days.

If, however, the D.A.O. does not agree that the patient's behaviour is sufficiently serious to warrant certification or removal to an observation unit, then the relatives may find that, contrary to their expectations and the suggestions of the family doctor, the sick person remains with them at home. But the decision is not always consistent with patients' behaviour. Because he cannot easily find an available bed, the D.A.O. may refuse to acknowledge that the disturbance is 'sufficiently serious'. Thus families may be bewildered by apparently contradictory advice or decisions from different people in authority, or by a system which on one occasion enables their sick relative to be removed, on another forbids his removal, when his behaviour is entirely similar. And though they live in East London and the mental hospital is at Epsom, in one crisis the patient may be taken to Battersea and in another to St. Pancras. For the relative and the patient, the period leading to admission may be full of prolonged anxiety and bewilderment.

Mrs. Martin was awakened by the police in the early hours of the morning. They informed her that her daughter was held at a police station in Kensington and that she should go there at once. 'How can I go there now? I'll go first thing in the morning.' 'Take a taxi,' said the police officer. Mrs. Martin could not afford that so she caught the first tube train next morning. The police officer at Kensington said he could not allow her to take her daughter home as she was too wild in her behaviour and explained that she would be certified. The daughter was taken by ambulance to Fulham observation unit where Mrs. Martin went to visit her the same evening. On the previous occasion that the daughter had broken down, a woman police officer travelled with her from East Anglia and then escorted her to Long Grove Hospital. Mrs Martin could not understand why 'you can never tell what they'll do'. The unpredictable behaviour of the patient makes it unlikely that the circumstances of admission will be closely similar even for the same patient on several consecutive occasions, but the unpredictability of the official handling of the situation makes it doubly difficult for patient or relatives to know what to expect from one crisis to the next. There is no simple standard way of entering the mental hospital.

There is a temptation to believe that much of the difficulty arises from the density of the population in London on the one hand, and the traditional East London abhorrence of institutional care on the other. But the description of mental hospitals in America, given by Clausen and Yarrow[1] in reports of their surveys in the Washington area, is so strikingly similar that it suggests that the confusion which clouds access to treatment for mental illness fulfils some disguised function.

> The hospitalization of the mentally ill persons whom we have studied was seldom accomplished efficiently. It is our impression that persons suffering from severe physical illness would usually come under medical care and have hospitalization arranged with much greater dispatch and much less lost motion. The lack of clarity as to what is happening and the family's inability to decide which way to turn is one important reason for the difficulty in dealing with mental illness. . . . The difficulty of knowing who in the community were the 'gatekeepers' to psychiatric care was, then, coupled with the wife's difficulty in arriving at a stable definition of the nature of her husband's problem. Some doctors, some clergymen, some policemen were able to recognize the nature of the husband's problem and to help deal with it effectively. Others were less well informed about mental illness, less well able to recognize

[1] Clausen, J. A., and Yarrow, M. R., 'Paths to the Mental Hospital'.

it and to assist the family. As a consequence, discontinuities of action were frequent, and paths to the hospital were beset with obstacles and traumata for husband and wife.

These words might well have been written about mental illness in East London.

The unexpected, the unpredictable and the intransigent are the daily lot of the Duly Authorized Officer (now to be known as the Mental Welfare Officer). Immediate and individual decisions involving heavy responsibility are a constant burden upon these officers, and they cannot be blamed for the fact that their work is often negative, custodial and inconsistent.

When the department is fully staffed—which, when retirement, sickness, training, holidays and evening and night work have been taken into consideration, is extremely rare —there are 24 Mental Welfare Officers in the London area. Clerical work, the courts and observation units must be covered, leaving fewer men in the field. In the evening (5–9) and at night (9 p.m.–9.30 a.m.) and on Saturday and Sunday there are only two men on duty for the London area.[1]

If the patient lives alone it is the duty of the officer to take charge of all valuables and money, see that the property is left safe and secure and that animals or birds are handed into somebody's care. As the call may be in the night this often means a second visit in daylight. If the patient has children and there is no one available to care for them the officer must contact the children's officer. Since this cannot always be done at night, and under the new regulations the children's homes are not bound to accept children brought by the Mental Welfare Officers, the D.A.O. is sometimes faced with taking babies and toddlers in the ambulance with the patient and leaving the children at the nearest police station. The police are empowered to leave children in the children's homes. As one Mental Welfare Officer remarked, expressing of course a purely personal

---

[1] From 1st Nov. 1960 the work was redistributed throughout the L.C.C. Divisions. See Appendix 3.

opinion, 'In spite of all the things about the old Poor Law in many ways it was more humane because it allowed us to do whatever was necessary at the time.'

The work makes heavy demands on this handful of officers and is complicated by innumerable physical and legal obstacles; it is not surprising that they have to struggle to keep it above minimum standards. It is a tribute to them that they so often maintain goodwill under such appalling difficulties.

There is confusion and inconsistency, therefore, in the way in which treatment is offered as well as in the way in which it is sought. On the one side the perception of the sick person's behaviour by himself, his relatives, work-mates and friends is partial and perhaps contradictory. The opinions held by one individual may be inconsistent in themselves and also opposed to those of others in contact with the sick person. Those not called upon to initiate action may see the sickness as mental disturbance more quickly and clearly than close relatives. On the other side, when the decision moves from the patient's immediate circle to the G.P., the welfare worker, the magistrate, the police or the D.A.O., each of them will perceive the patient differently, not only because individuals differ, but also because the limits imposed upon them by their work may lead each of them to decide on a different course for the patient. Their perceptions are slanted by the pressures of their work.

Admission to mental hospital is generally a confused, slow, and clumsy process which may reach a sudden bewildering climax. It begins with the gradual and reluctant recognition of illness. Then, sometimes for years, relatives may try to protect the sick man or woman within the family. When at last the strain becomes intolerable or some incident brings the illness forcibly to the notice of society, then admission to hospital, with or without the patient's consent, becomes inevitable. In such a crisis it is not surprising if at times the dignity and feelings of the sick person are overlooked. But it is equally true that the distress which this causes must make both patients and relatives all the more reluctant to seek treatment.

Those who are sick, yet successful in their wish to evade treatment, may in the end be less fortunate than the patients already described. But even if they never find relief from their sickness, nor their relatives and neighbours release from anxiety and disturbance, the mentally ill who remain in the community without treatment can cling, if only precariously, to the rights and duties of responsibility.

The manner of the mental patient's admission often foreshadows the loss of freedom and respect characteristic of his new status. His wishes may be ignored, his opinions or objections discounted. He is treated as not responsible. If he acknowledges his mental illness he must accept the loss of his responsible role in society. In the next chapter some of the patients' experiences in hospital and their reaction to them are described and discussed.

III

THE PATIENT IN HOSPITAL

IN the last chapter we described how the patients came to enter hospital. They often did so reluctantly, and though most of them were nominally voluntary patients they had often been brought to hospital without their full consent. For the psychiatrist this creates a moral dilemma; he has the same desire as anyone else to respect the liberty of the individual, but equally, it would seem to him a breach of his professional trust to allow serious illness to go untreated. In imposing his judgement upon a reluctant patient, the psychiatrist hopes that as the patient experiences the value of treatment he will very quickly win his co-operation. If these hopes were realized it would be misguided to protest too much against the way in which patients are sometimes brought to hospital against their will. But in practice it seems that the resentment aroused in patients and their relatives by the manner of admission often prevents co-operation with the hospital. The interviews with these 86 patients show that their response to treatment is often greatly affected by the mode of their admission, and the length of their stay is influenced by their attitude to hospital as much as by the progress of treatment.

Twenty-three of the 86 patients spent a year or more at Long Grove: eight of them, all certified, were still there at the completion of the survey. At the other extreme, there were 13 who left after less than a week, and one who at the last moment refused to enter hospital at all. Either they refused to admit that they were ill and insisted on their family accepting them back, or their families themselves could not bear their absence, and agreed that the hospital was no place for them. In between are two very different kinds of patients: those who left after a single period of some weeks or months of treatment (24), and those who were in and out of the hospital several times during the year (25).

Those who stayed the longest and the shortest time in hospital had in several ways more in common with each other than with the two intermediate groups. They tended to be the most seriously ill, to have poor prospects of recovery, and to have little or no awareness of themselves and their situation: some have retreated into hallucinations and fantasy; others have never emerged from it. They also included more of the oldest and youngest patients. Amongst the patients who stayed longest were some very young people, who had very little grasp of reality, and also those senile people for whom admission to a mental hospital was a final step.

For old people who are married, this is the worst tragedy that can befall them. Mr. Fane is a dignified old gentleman, but it is impossible to make him smile. He is in one hospital, his wife in another. He is taken to see her about once a month when the weather is good and transport available. They never see each other without other people round about them. He knows that his wife will never recover her physical health and that she will die in hospital. He knows that he will never go home again and that in fact his personal possessions have been sold. At first he would not speak, but gradually he said a few things. 'All these things are sent to try us.' 'They do try us—very hard. You don't understand why. I'm just waiting to go now. Can't think why I'm still here. She's still here too, in that other hospital. They take me to see her sometimes. She don't recognize people and she can't speak. I think she knows it's me and I can see she's pleased, but she can't tell you about it. When they took her away and I was left on my own I went queer in the head you know. Well, it's understandable, isn't it? It's good of you to call. No, I don't want anything—there's nothing you can do for me, thank you all the same.' His fine face is set in a pattern of resigned grief, but he never complains. He is not bitter and he is not aware that he can no longer smile. He waits patiently and accepts the orders of the male nurse without rancour; he never comments on a system which separates an elderly couple and dictates that a man and his wife shall sleep under separate roofs and see each other when and how it is convenient to others, because they had the misfortune to fall ill in an impoverished but companionable old age. (The brother of a younger patient, commenting on other elderly folk who had been separated in this way, said with some bitterness, 'And we're supposed to be the ones what's ignorant and don't know how to do things properly—why I'd hang myself sooner than do a thing like that, separate a couple that's been together all those years and so used to each other, it's criminal. An animal would have a better sense of decency than that.')

The patients who stayed longest in hospital did not, as a whole, accept the hospital as willingly as the two intermediate groups. They remained, rather, because they had no choice: they were certified, or they had no relative willing to accept them home. Those who discharged themselves within a week, of course, did not accept the hospital at all. They or their families reacted violently to other disturbed patients and to authority. Sometimes relatives brought the patient straight home, without completing the formalities of discharge.

The brother-in-law of one patient, for instance, was sent by the family on the second visiting day, and brought him straight home. The patient himself remarked 'When I got back to London I phoned the doctor but he was out. I told the secretary I'd rather work it all out for myself, and that I was all right.'

Mr. Pavey read between the lines of his wife's letter that all was not well. It was not a visiting day but he drove down in a relative's car and insisted on seeing his wife—the more opposition he encountered the more frantic he became. When at last his wife appeared, he discovered she had been moved into a locked ward with disturbed patients because of her *physical* condition. He took her for a walk in the grounds, bundled her into the car and drove back home, where he gave up his job for three months and nursed his wife himself, incurring a debt which ran into hundreds of pounds.

Mrs. Brown, shocked at the sight of the patients among whom her helpless husband would spend his time, fretted herself into a frenzy. She could not sleep the night after his admission, and the following morning hired a car and fetched him home.

Sometimes the patients themselves were so repelled by their first impression of the hospital that they asked immediately for discharge. 'I arrived at five in the afternoon, and at eight the next morning I put in my notice to quit,' said Mr. Porter. And Mr. Churchley felt at once that Long Grove was not for him: 'I was shown into the ward, and several of them was in bed. A man got up, stark naked he was, and came over to me. He shook hands and said, "How d'you do? I'm the American ambassador"—so then I knew I'd come to the right place. I said to the fellow in the bed opposite. "He's a bit gone, isn't he?" and he wouldn't answer me. It was only afterwards I found out he was deaf and dumb. Then there was a bit of a fight and nobody took any notice. I thought "you could be knocked out and nobody would bother" and anyway there's nothing wrong with me like that, so I decided to get out of it. If I'd stayed there I'd have gone mad myself.'

These patients rejected the hospital out of hand: they did not accept that they were ill, and were repelled by the institutional life with which they were confronted. The 25 who had been admitted more than once in the course of the year were more tolerant of the hospital as an institution, and made use of it in the crises of their illness. But they did not really accept it as an opportunity for treatment. They had come to terms with their illness in their own way. They led restless, disrupted lives, but had learned how to survive outside hospital so long as they could use it as a place of refuge in times of particular stress. Some of them repeatedly struggled back into the community even though they had neither friend nor relative to help them. These patients became 'old lags' of the hospital, neither accepting nor rejecting it, but adapting themselves philosophically to its routine. Most of them discharged themselves from hospital without medical approval.

The remaining 24 patients accepted hospital treatment, at least for a time, and were discharged within a year. More of them had been brought to hospital as a result of mounting problems, but had at least one relative, and often several, who very much needed them at home. As a whole, they accepted the hospital and submitted themselves to treatment more readily than the others. Though they might have objected violently to their admission, they were sufficiently conventional to obey the rules of the institution in which they found themselves, and they generally waited for the hospital to take the initiative in their discharge. Several of this group had held positions where some self-discipline and authority were required and they were, therefore, more used to accepting rules. Among this group of conformers who, though they might not like the way it worked, accepted the principle that administrative systems are right and proper, were two women who did not particularly accommodate to this pattern. They were obedient because they were by nature excessively timid and submissive and would not have dreamed of fighting admission or proposing discharge. Behind a thin screen of non-opposition and submission they were then both able to carry on a delicate child-like life where everything was 'nice' like it used to be and only occasionally menaced by the horrific fantasies which they could not tolerate or accept as part of themselves. 'I don't want to say such dreadful things, something gets in my head and I hear it swearing and saying the most terrible things. I'm sure I don't want to be like that to any-one, really I don't—we were brought up very respectable and you never heard a word out of place in our house.' So one sought to reassure herself that the monsters were no-thing to do with her. The other woman lives on memories of the farm where she spent her childhood, and of the animals with which she could communicate because they did not terrify her like human beings.

The patients, therefore, differed in their reaction to the hospital according to the length of their stay, and the frequency of their admission. Each group tends to have a core of patients of a characteristic type, together with those who are in the process of coming from or going to one of the other groups. But movement in some directions is more likely than in others. Patients who discharge themselves within a week of admission are more likely to return for a long while, if at all, than to become recurrent inmates of the hospital. Nor will they be likely to accept single fairly short periods of treatment. Many of those who spent from a week to a year in hospital will never return, unless age or the loss of those who care for them forces them into hospital, but a few may be at the beginning of a career of repeated admissions.

With these variations, the length of stay in hospital seems to particularize characteristic groups of patients. They differ in the way in which they adapt themselves to the routine of an institution, if they adapt at all. And they con-tain differing proportions of men and women, married and single.

There is a marked tendency for the patients to concen-trate in a particular group according to sex and marital status. The highest proportion of single women remain in hospital over a year, while the single men tend most often to have been admitted repeatedly in the course of a year. The married women are predominantly in hospital for one period of weeks or months, and do not return, while the married men are concentrated amongst those who discharged themselves within a week. Only the widowed and divorced do not show this trend, there being none who were discharged within a week.

TABLE II

LENGTH OF STAY IN HOSPITAL, ACCORDING TO SEX AND MARITAL STATUS OF PATIENTS

Length of Stay	Men		Women		
	Single	Married	Single	Married	Widowed or separated
One year or longer*	28%	11%	50%	14%	33%
Repeated admissions within one year ..	56%	22%	15%	22%	42%
One week to one year (one visit only)	11%	23%	20%	57%	25%
Less than one week	5%	44%	15%	7%	—%
Total %	100%	100%	100%	100%	100%
Number ..	18	20	20	14	12

* Eight patients were still in hospital at the time this study was completed. A widower and a separated man have been omitted from this table.

Although these percentages are based on small numbers and might not be confirmed by a larger sample, Table II suggests that length of stay in hospital is unlikely to be simply a function of the severity of the illness. Men appear to be less tolerant of hospital than women; they tend either to repudiate it at once, or to remain there only for short periods at a time. And the single people tend to stay longer, or return more frequently, than the married. Few husbands or wives remain in hospital for more than a year: they are likely to be the most irreplaceable at home. The single not only have a greater chance of getting into hospital, but they tend to stay there longer also.[1]

[1] For further discussion of this point see Appendix 2.

So the sex and marital status of a patient appears to influence how long he will remain in hospital. The length of his stay is also associated with the number of visitors he receives. Frequent visits soon after admission often went with attempts to remove the patient from hospital. Since the visiting days at Long Grove are Sunday and Monday,[1] several patients who remained in hospital only three days had groups of visitors on two occasions. On the other hand, amongst the chronic patients, if the family made no effort to secure a discharge within the first few weeks, they were likely to remain in hospital for over a year. The patients who stayed longest had fewer visitors than those who remained in hospital for one period only of a week to a year, and only slightly more than those who were admitted repeatedly.

Yet it is not possible to say categorically that those who are most visited have most relatives, least illness, and the best prognosis, and are most likely to be taken home. Nor, on the contrary, are those least visited likely to stay longest, though with every month that a patient remains in hospital this is more likely to be true. Evidence from an analysis of discharge and visiting figures made by Brown showed '35% of schizophrenic patients admitted to two London mental hospitals in 1950–51 were retained for two years or more. There was a positive relationship between such retention and a lack of visitors in the first two months' stay in hospital.'[2] But a reduction in the length of stay by non-visited patients was achieved in both hospitals five years later, so the effect of visiting cannot be considered in isolation.

Some relatives who have 'put away' a patient with the utmost relief will follow a persistent pattern of over-anxious visiting and attention in order to assuage feelings of guilt. Other relatives who are deeply devoted to the patient and grieve for him at home cannot bear to see him

[1] This was altered to Thursday at the end of 1960.
[2] Brown, G., 'Social factors influencing length of hospital stay of schizophrenic patients'.

in such surroundings and may never visit. Isobel Griffiths' mother has not seen her for more than a year. Each pines separately for the other. Isobel constantly says, 'I want to go home to help my Mum,' and her mother appears to be permanently distraught because of Isobel's absence even after two years.

The relative's feelings towards the patient and the hospital apart, visiting is both uncomfortable and expensive. The journey to Long Grove by public transport will take at least 1½ hours. It can mean a bus ride, a journey on the tube with an awkward change at Bank Station,[1] followed by a train journey and another bus trip or 20 minutes' walk. Some people prefer to find their way by the Green Line coach route to Epsom. But there is no simple and direct route to the hospital, and it is practically impossible to make the return journey for less than 7s. Buses and trains only link up on Sundays for a brief period, and travel grants are only issued sporadically to certain people on National Assistance, in spite of continued recommendations by the Superintendent. A special coach to be hired regularly was refused a licence because it would run on routes 'covered by alternative public transport'. The journey to the hospital is a physical hazard and worrying expense for old-age pensioners, and many other relatives besides. Visitors to the patients in the sample spent an average of £1 on each visit. On a Sunday the relatives leave home too early for lunch and return rather too late for tea and often very exhausted. Sandwiches and snacks add to the cost and complications. Under the circumstances it is surprising that the relatives come as often as they do, even in the winter. However, though the frequency of visits is affected as much by expense and practical difficulties as by concern for the patient, it seems that those who have most visitors, especially soon after admission, will be least likely to become habitual inmates of the hospital.

[1] Elderly relatives unable to manoeuvre the spiral iron staircase between the Central and Northern lines were forced to travel by bus.

At the time when this study was made, a voluntary patient could discharge himself, on his own initiative or that of his relatives, without the approval of the hospital, provided he gave three days' notice. Alternatively the hospital might discharge him, or at least acquiesce in his discharge. Many of the patients who had been certified on admission were later regraded as voluntary, in order that they might enjoy more freedom, and so could also discharge themselves against the hospital's advice, if they wished. More than a third of them did so. Altogether, nearly half the patients who had returned home when this study was made, left against the advice of the hospital. Those who were in hospital for only a week or less, of course, all did so: they virtually repudiated treatment. And those who had been in hospital over a year were mostly discharged with the hospital's approval: they would not have stayed so long if they had not acquiesced in the hospital's authority over them. These two groups would be expected to differ in the manner of their discharge. But the contrast is as great

TABLE III

MANNER OF DISCHARGE, ACCORDING TO LENGTH OF STAY
IN HOSPITAL

Discharged	*Length of Stay*			
	One year or longer	One week –one year	Less than one week	Repeated admissions in one year
With hospital approval..	75%	79%	8%	32%
Without hospital approval	25%	21%	92%	68%
Total %	100%	100%	100%	100%
Number	16	24	13	25

Note: Eight patients were still in hospital when the study was completed.

between the two intermediate groups: those who stayed several weeks or months, and did not afterwards return, and those who returned repeatedly to hospital in the course of the year. The different manner of discharge of the two groups of patients, who spent from a week to a year in hospital, seems to be associated with differences in the nature of their illness. The difference, however, is not so much in the form of the illness as in its origin.

The patients who were admitted repeatedly to hospital and later discharged themselves, tend to have been ill since childhood: they have always been abnormal, and they will almost certainly always be different from the rest of society. They do not wish at heart to become normal:[1] their attitude to employment is unconventional, and they have either never had a job, or worked only erratically. They will probably continue to enter hospital at intervals for the rest of their lives. Some of them have learned to accept their illness and manage it. They do not expect miracles from the hospital: they are neither for it nor against it. In the face of the routine of such an institution, like Gulley Jimson they 'take it as they find themselves, and give their best attention to something else'. These recurrent inmates of the hospital might be called 'born psychotics'.

By contrast many of the patients who were discharged by the hospital after some weeks or months of treatment give the impression that they might never have entered hospital at all but for some particularly distressing experience, or some physical disability in addition to their mental confusion. One man had had appalling experiences during the war, which haunted him. Three of the women broke down after childbirth and two others when they realized that they could never have children. Two of the elderly patients had been greatly distressed when they were forced to retire against their wish: three others suffered from physical disabilities of old age. If they had been more fortunate, if their physical health had been better, many of these patients

[1] They seem to repudiate or to be indifferent to the dominant values of society.

might never have entered hospital. They became psychotic only through force of circumstances.

The distinction is a fine one: it is difficult to determine how far tragic circumstances cause breakdown, and how far illness invites misfortune. But where it can be drawn, it may reveal a very important difference in the nature of the illness, and the probable outcome of treatment. The 'born psychotic' is likely to come to terms with his illness, rather than be rid of it: the hospital to him is less a source of treatment than a place of refuge in times of crisis. Those who become psychotic through force of circumstance are more amenable to treatment, and more likely to make a genuine recovery.

For many, admission to a mental hospital is only an episode in a long struggle with their disabilities. They leave hospital to face familiar problems, sometimes alone, sometimes under the care of a wife or husband, mother or sister, devoted to them. Others, more fortunate, return home competent to resume a place in conventional society. But for all of them, admission to hospital is a public acknowledgement of an illness which profoundly affects their relationships with their family and the society in which they live. Their judgement, their competence to handle their responsibilities, even their feelings and wishes, become suspect, and they are liable to find everything they may say or do discounted as mere aberrations.[1] Because of this, few people will readily accept the implication of becoming a hospital patient, and their experience in hospital will in turn affect the way in which they regard their illness. The attitudes of the patients, of their relatives and of society towards their illness and its treatment, everywhere influences how the mentally ill manage their lives, how they get into hospital, and how they leave it.

---

[1] The problem of scapegoating, especially in new housing blocks, requires special study. Some patients who had actually been robbed found it difficult to obtain a hearing because they were suspected of having paranoid delusions. Another man said, 'When you come out of a mental hospital you have to be twice as sensible as other people—what someone else could do would be pointed out as daft if I did it.'

IV

PERCEPTION OF MENTAL ILLNESS

IF you had been in a mental hospital, would you admit it?
'No, not really,' Mr. Jackson said. He had entered hospital
at his own request, encouraged by the successful treatment of one of his relatives, but he still recognized what a
damaging confession it could be. 'If people were discussing
mental hospitals, I'd defend them and explain about mental
illness, but I wouldn't exactly say I'd been to one myself.
People think you're daft or something. They don't understand that you can be mixed up about one thing that
bothers you and the rest of your mind perfectly clear. And
they think all mental hospitals are like that film *The Snake
Pit*.'

We are most of us afraid of mental illness. Our feelings
towards the mentally ill may be tainted with contempt, or
we may try to protect ourselves against this fear and antipathy by keeping the sick at a distance. We ignore them as
people, discount what they say, or humour them in a way
which discredits or undervalues them even more. These
responses to the mentally ill anger and frighten them, and it
becomes more and more difficult for normal and abnormal
to communicate. The wall of disbelief closes around the
mental patient, leaving him utterly frustrated, bitter or
cynical. 'When you've been in one of those places nobody
believes you,' remarked one married woman, 'they say "it's
only her mind, take no notice".'

Many of the mentally ill themselves share the popular
conception of mental illness, and therefore deny that they

42

are ill. Others look for an explanation in physical terms. Even those who can accept that they are mentally ill, tend to speak of it as if defending themselves against criticism.

The denial of their illness by mental patients is rather similar to the way in which people suffering from partial paralysis will refuse to admit it, even when they cannot use their limbs at all. But it is necessarily more complicated, because their illness, by definition, is a disturbance of judgement. Some of the patients interviewed simply denied aggressively that there was anything the matter with them. Others saw themselves as the victims of a sinister plot.

> 'There's nothing wrong with me, mate. It's these bloody doctors, dragging your things off and messing you about. There's nothing wrong with me. My daughter will take me home next week, I'm quite fit. I've been a hard-working woman all my life. I'm not having any more of it, I'm telling you.'

> 'I am perfect. When I go back to heaven to be with God, He will destroy the whole world to punish the people who sent me to hospital.'

Six patients denied altogether that they were ill, and three others also denied it, but were willing to discuss it at the same time. Indeed, the mentally ill are no more consistent in their attitude to their illness, than is society in its attitude towards them. Many of the patients recognized that there was something the matter with them, but denied its nature. They felt they suffered only from overwork, nerves, stomach troubles, tumours.

> 'It's all nerves really. It's like sciatica—that's the sciatic nerve. Or when you get the toothache. It's all to do with the ends of the nerves. There's something wrong with them that makes you feel that you've got a pain somewhere. That's why I say you ought to do away with that word "mental" altogether.'

> 'There's nothing mental about me. They shouldn't mix the lunatics with the nerve cases. I came out of it. If I'd stayed, I'd have gone up the wall like some of them. It's terrible for an ordinary man.'

43

'I get these terrible pains in my stomach. Stands to reason there must be something (physical) causing it.'

Other patients, however, interpreted their condition in terms which come much closer to the professional understanding of mental illness. But they tended to emphasize causes outside themselves—in personal tragedies or childhood experiences—which helped to restore their confidence in their fundamental normality.

'I was laid up with 'flu, that brought it on the first time. I've had a lot of worry. I lost my husband in an accident, and my relatives during the war. I think the war turned a lot of people's brains. I felt a bit light-headed, and everything started turning black and coming at me.'

'The beginning of it was when I was fifteen, but you see these things go back to your childhood. After my mother died when I was a nipper, my sister looked after me for a bit, then they put some of us in an orphanage. Do you know what it's like in an orphanage? It's just a lot of hands doing a lot of things to a lot of kids. Well, then my Dad had me back again to live with him. I reckon a lot of it was to do with my father. I don't blame him, but he didn't know how to bring up children. He had no idea. He fetched himself up and expected me to do the same. I didn't really learn things properly the way I ought, and I think that's how it all started.'

This understanding of their illness in terms of childhood deprivation or traumatic experiences was commoner amongst the younger patients, who may have read accounts of psychoanalytic theory.[1] One young man, though he also saw the origins of his illness in his upbringing, interpreted his difficulties in terms of misconceived values rather than neglect. He, too, grew up in an orphanage.

'You see, at the orphanage I never had anything that belonged to me, and when I'd got money of my own and started earning, I'd stand in front of shops and got what I call the fancies. I'd have a fancy for this or a fancy for that and I must dash in and buy it—sometimes lots of things, and take them home with

---

[1] Several patients borrowed psychiatric books regularly from the public library.

me. Well, it took me a long time to work out that it was *not having* the thing which bothered me. Once I'd bought it and got it home it didn't make me happy. I wasn't interested in it any more and I laid it aside. That's how I came to have masses and masses of things in my room. All material things, you see. I had to have everything at once. They piled up around me and that's what sort of cut me off. It was as if I was at the bottom of a very deep well and all the things I'd bought and piled up around me were the bricks of the well. Each thing was a brick. I was at the bottom looking up and wanting to get out. I wanted to know people and understand them and get on with them, but I couldn't because I was at the bottom of the well with my things piled round me. Now the spiritual things need brightening up and bringing to the front and then I can get on with people all right.'

Out of this interpretation of his illness he also built up a philosophy about modern society.

'All this racing about, you run past your own mind and lose yourself. Then it's not all this rushing about, it's grab, grab and *things* all the time. And the pictures—you get to thinking you're in the film chucking your weight about like the hero and it's no good. The world wants to slow down and think about something else.'

Thus, in part, he placed the responsibility for his illness on the false values of society.

There were, finally, several patients who did not deny that they were mentally ill nor look for an explanation in terms of what had happened to them. They had ceased to blame the doctors, the world, their parents, God, physical diseases or some other scapegoat. They accepted their illness without needing to justify or excuse their difficulties. Mr. Kerstein has now reached this position though he feels that the last shreds of understanding still elude him.

'Talking to people who've been the same as you is a great factor. But I can never quite get to the bottom of my own illness. I can see other people's, but when I get to thinking about myself, somehow or other I never *quite* get it sorted out.'

He has spent since 1941 thinking about his own case. At one time he went to several psychiatric lectures and this provided a basis for his subsequent thoughts. But it is still a battle to keep out of hospital. 'Sometimes,' he said, 'when I'm going to work, my legs go all weak and I feel I can't go on. Four times recently I've fought it off now and managed to get to work and then I get a bit better. If I ever start thinking I'll go into hospital again then I've had it, I'm bound to go.' But he always told himself, 'However hard it is I've been through it before,' and that steadied him.

Mr. Kerstein was more concerned to manage his illness, and to understand the situation in which it placed him, than to trace its cause. And it had taken many years of courage and patience to achieve such insight.

Just as the mentally ill sometimes deny their illness, sometimes explain it in ways which disguise its nature from themselves, sometimes accept it so long as they can attribute it to external misfortunes rather than weakness in themselves, so their relatives tend to evade the acknowledgement of illness in their family. How far they do so depends in part on the closeness of their relationship to the patient.

Where there is deep affection, other members of the family will try to find an interpretation of the patient's behaviour which admits it as normal. These interpretations may be stretched to the limit of plausibility, and only finally abandoned when the patient enters hospital. Hence admission to hospital, rather than the behaviour itself, determines that a person is mentally disturbed. Occasionally, a relative would remark '*looking back*, I can see now it had been coming on a long time'. But the admission of the patient to hospital first shocked them into awareness, and the explanation 'mentally ill' was then applied retrospectively. It is afterwards very difficult for them to recover a state of mind in which the patient's behaviour is not so labelled. The illness is only seen as illness after a painful struggle. One wife, faced with the choice of siding with her hallucinated paranoic husband, accepting his hallucinations and thereby

46

risking her own sanity, or rejecting him as 'mad', swung first in one direction and then in the other. She suffered much mental and physical anguish with fits of weeping and insomnia. 'Those people *do* act funny to him, I've seen them myself throwing things at him,' she declared on one occasion, but on another she wept when he spoke of the Evil Influence getting him and said sharply, 'What d'you want to talk like that for?' Turning to the interviewer she continued, 'I can't get no rest with him sitting up in case they get him in his sleep and we can't leave the grandchildren alone with him in the house.'

Even severely aggressive behaviour may be minimized by the relatives. A mother, referring to a shooting incident in which her son had been involved, said, 'The other boys picked on him and naturally he felt he had to defend himself, and liked to carry the gun about to feel safe. And anyway he only shot through the man's sleeve.' She was contradicted by another relative who said the man had been wounded.

A woman described her sister's behaviour as slightly confused, and blamed it all on a bump on the head and some 'injections which disagreed with her'. But her husband was quite definite about his sister-in-law's state of mind, and recited a list of aberrations which included throwing food away every day for fear of contamination, running about the streets and getting lost, attacks on imaginary burglars and similar difficult behaviour. 'She was peculiar for years before them injections,' he insisted.

If the patient and his family have been on bad terms before his illness, then unexpected behaviour may well be an excuse for a break. The behaviour is then labelled as 'peculiar', 'wicked' or openly described as being 'madness'. Relatives-in-law, too, are more consciously aware of the patient's abnormal behaviour, more outspoken in describing it, readier to admit it, and do not grope for external and non-hereditary causes to explain it. Blood relatives often do not 'see' the patient's behaviour as mental illness. They are besides more chary of openly facing something which they fear as a stigma on their family, and search in their minds for the 'bang on the head' or other occurrence which would explain the patient's behaviour.

Those who feel no need to respect the feelings of the mentally ill, tend to describe the illness in mocking or derogatory phrases—'off his chump', 'queer in the head', or —amongst the young people—'gone bonkers', 'doing his nut'. People who are closer to the mentally ill use gentler euphemisms. Henry is 'troubled', Alice is 'in a distant state just now', George is 'not himself' or 'not with us'.

Relatives, therefore, tend to perceive mental illness less readily, less clearly, and less brutally, the closer their tie with the patient. And it seems that social distance may similarly influence the attitude of neighbours. This study was not designed to sample the awareness and interpretation of mental illness by the community at large, but one instance came to light in which neighbours showed a similar difficulty in perceiving mental illness amongst those with whom they most identified themselves.

Two families were interviewed in a street where there also lived five mental patients to whom they were not related. Three of these patients, at least, were equally and obviously ill. One had moved into the neighbourhood since marriage, one had been born there, and the third belonged to a household with which the two neighbouring families were acquainted. The two families were hostile to the patient who had not been born there, and would not let their children have anything to do with him. 'Of course he doesn't come from here. You never know when they're going to turn nasty, do you? All that family is funny.' Towards the second, they were tolerant and sympathetic. She was 'one of us, poor thing', and it never occurred to them to keep their children away from her. They did not realize that the third was ill at all. Nor did they recognize the illness of the two other patients in the street, with whom they were also on speaking terms—though in them the illness was less obtrusive. It has been suggested that, where life is lived at extremely close quarters with a large number of other people, certain habits of 'not seeing' and unawareness, or at least lack of *conscious* awareness are developed to facilitate an easy communal life where it might otherwise be intolerable. Perhaps the mentally sick, like the Emperor in the fairy tale, are clothed and protected by social scotoma.

The degree to which mental illness is accepted largely determines how willingly a man will enter hospital and his family will let him go. The way in which he understands his illness will influence what he expects to find there. And his experiences of hospital, in turn, help to form a conception of what mental illness is and what it entails.

All these interpretations and justifications seek to resolve a painful choice. For though acknowledgement of his illness relieves a patient of responsibility for his social incompetence, and so from the judgement of his fellow men, it entails a loss of freedom and status which is scarcely less humiliating. His attitude to freedom and responsibility govern the interpretation of his illness and both together form the basis of his attitude to hospital prior to his admission.

V

ATTITUDES TO HOSPITAL

A HOSPITAL is an institution caring for large numbers of people. In any such institution the individual tends to be discounted in the interests of uniform and convenient administration. As Erving Goffman has pointed out, the routine imposed by such an administration can be formidable when large numbers of people must be organized to live together.[1] He describes how entry to any total institution is accompanied by a period of humiliation, while the new entrants learn to behave so as to facilitate the routine, and not to bring trouble on themselves by asserting their right to freedom. This is as true of a mental hospital as any other institution. It makes demands which would strain the patience of the most stable person, but which are intolerable to someone who cannot easily reconcile himself even to the conditions of everyday life. On entering the hospital he is expected to conform to a discipline and routine far more rigid than anything he has previously encountered. His unconventional habits are trimmed to fit the constriction of an institution. The many facets of his personality are clipped into categories which coincide with diagnostic labels. He becomes a case, rather than a person. As one patient described it, 'When the doctor left the room I nipped up quickly and looked at what he'd written. "Inadequate psychopath" it said, and when I got out of hospital I went straight to the library and looked it up, and I tell you I didn't like it.' Another man said, 'Hebephrenic, what the hell would that be?'

[1] Goffman, E., 'On the Characteristics of Total Institutions'.

Once he has become an inmate of the hospital, labelled and docketed, the patient may find it very difficult to communicate at all with the staff, as one person to another. Mr. Porter, for example, remembers with great indignation, how, when he entered hospital as a voluntary patient bringing with him a letter of introduction, he was treated as if he were not present. This first puzzled him and then infuriated him. The porter instructed the patient's wife where to enter the building, looking at her over Mr. Porter's outstretched hand and the letter of introduction. When Mr. Porter objected the man continued to address Mrs. Porter and referred her to another hospital employee who behaved in exactly the same way.

The experience of a general practitioner illustrates ironically the frustrations of attempting to secure a hearing once you are perceived as mentally ill. The doctor arrived late at a mental hospital to attend one of a series of special lectures. He found his way to the central quadrangle, where the lecture room was situated, only to discover that the door had been locked at the commencement of the lecture. Without hesitation he walked to a window overlooking the quadrangle, where he could see a colleague listening to the lecture and tapped gently, indicating that he wished to be let in. The only response of the doctor inside the building was to turn his head sharply and move his chair forward out of line with the window. The late-comer then returned to the door and was about to slip a note underneath when he thought better of it. He began to make his way back to the main building in search of a key, and noticed a nurse crossing the far corner of the square. Anxious not to miss any more of the lecture he unwisely ran towards her, calling and waving a hand. She swept into a near-by building and swiftly locked the door behind her. Turning once again towards the main building, he observed a neatly dressed man approaching him. They walked quietly towards each other and smiled. The doctor was about to ask for a master key when the man inquired, 'Are you one of them or one of us?' He could only admit, regretfully, that he was one of them.

The ways in which the staff avoid or ignore the patients, for fear of some disturbance in their routine, tends to provoke the very reaction which they are trying to forestall. Nurses in the hospital can be seen, when they are alone, moving swiftly away from a patient, which provokes the patient into pursuit. Similarly a group of nurses, seeing a patient get agitated with one of their colleagues, will close in round the disturbed and frightened patient who will then thresh about in terror. The patient's violence is afterwards quoted as a justification for closing in on him in numbers.

Routines are taken for granted which arouse violent antipathy in the patients. The patients feel that they are being deliberately punished or humiliated. A patient, for instance, is refused the opportunity to shave: to him it is an affront to his self-respect; to the hospital it is merely part of the routine—Tuesday is not a shaving day. Moreover, there is often no time to explain, and a request, harmless enough in itself, may be the last straw in a series of incidents which a patient feels were deliberately planned to destroy his individuality and self-respect. The nurse who brusquely demanded the origin of Mr. Porter's war-wound scars was completing the routine admission inquiries, but to Mr. Porter, already smouldering with resentment from the three previous people who had either ignored him or treated him as an inanimate object, this was a further inexplicable insult to add to a mounting tide of humiliation. When he asked to apply for discharge the next day, the charge nurse was very indignant.

The restrictions and routine, the locked doors, the refusal to listen, may leave the patient with a real sense of imprisonment. He may react with a panic which only confirms the staff in the correctness of their measures: the man is violent and must be carefully supervised. One patient recalled his first admission to hospital, many years ago: 'I didn't know it *was* a hospital at all, it was just as though I'd been kidnapped. When you get inside and you're locked in, you get a funny feeling. Well anyone resents being locked in as though they've been naughty. Apparently I was carrying on very badly when I first went in. I wasn't really carrying on at the hospital, it was all those people wandering about with keys and whistles, rushing here and there. I thought it was a concentration camp at first. I let off steam.' Only as he learned to tolerate the imposition of institutional life, did he discover how to use the hospital as a temporary refuge, with whose help he could survive the disabilities of his illness.

A patient's reaction to hospital depends in part, therefore, on his tolerance of the characteristic restrictions and impersonality of an institutional routine. But his experiences after admission seldom create an attitude towards hospital: they modify an attitude which was already there. Whatever happens to him in hospital can only confirm or destroy the fears, hopes or illusions with which he entered it. His attitude to hospital is closely related to his interpretation of his illness.

The previous chapter described how attitudes to illness range from uncompromising denial to unequivocal acceptance. At one extreme are those who claim 'There's nothing wrong with me'. Next are those who allow that they are ill, but insist that they suffer only from physical complaints. Others will admit that they are mentally ill, but feel the need to excuse it—anyone would break down under what they went through; it's their parents' fault; the fault of a materialistic society. And lastly, a few can not only see that they are ill, but accept its nature without needing to excuse their difficulties.

Those who come to hospital denying their illness most vehemently naturally have an unco-operative, or even hostile, attitude to the hospital. They do not require much stimulus to make them return home without delay or, if they cannot leave, remain in a spirit of entrenched obstructiveness. They seize upon every similarity to defend their belief that the hospital is a prison. Locks, keys, whistles, hospital clothes, hospital numbers and the loss of certain rights readily provoke such feelings. Furthermore, those who enter hospital fearing that they have but a wavering grasp on their personal identity find no support in a regime which discounts it.

When such patients seek discharge shortly after arrival it is common for a member of the hospital personnel to say 'You haven't given it a fair chance', forgetting that the patient does not base his attitude solely upon his recent brief experience of living in the hospital. This experience is often the closing sentence of a long story. Even when the hospital staff know that this is so, they tend always to behave *as if* the moment the patient crossed the hospital threshold were the opening paragraph. Similarly they are inclined to believe that because the patient is *in* the hospital here and now, therefore his present environment is confined to the hospital. The patient knows that he brings much of his environment with him, and that his thoughts continue to be centred on the place from which he has come. It may be more real to him than the hospital around him.

When the 'denial' patient says, 'There's nothing wrong with me' he implies several things such as 'I am blameless and capable of judging for myself, therefore there is no reason to take away my freedom'. It follows that if there is nothing wrong with him and yet his relatives and the doctors have put him in hospital, then either there is some terrible misunderstanding, or the relatives and the doctors are his worst enemies. 'They want to get rid of me' commonly goes with 'There's nothing wrong with me' and 'The doctors swindled me, they said this was a convalescent home'. The hospital itself is spoken of as 'prison', 'the loony house', 'one of *those* places', it may be, 'fit for people who are lunatics', but, 'they've no right to put *me* with cases like that'. The stronger the denial of illness, the greater the fear of it. This group of patients could not tolerate the presence of disturbed patients and frequently discharged themselves within three days of admission. 'If I stopped there a day longer I'd have been like that myself.' Absolute denial of illness goes with unqualified rejection of hospital.

Those who seek to justify their illness are open to persuasion by their hospital experience. If their wishes are fulfilled then their enthusiasm for hospital is extravagant; if they are not, then they are disappointed and disillusioned. Those who justified their mental illness by referring to undue stress, entered hospital expecting that it would be a convalescent home, a haven of peace and rest where they could quietly recuperate, tended and cherished by the nurses. When they were asked to wash up, dust the day room, or complete some other household task, they became indignant, especially if they were housewives. In their view polishing floors had nothing to do with therapy. 'If I'm well enough to do housework here I might as well do it at home,' said one patient, while another working in the laundry said, 'I might as well do this outside and get paid for it.'

However, some of the patients who felt 'anyone would break down, I need a rest' were admitted in summer time to the small villas separated from the main hospital. This was much more what they expected, and they responded with enthusiastic appreciation. 'It's marvellous,' said Mrs. Fryers, 'as good as being away for a holiday. Just like Butlins.' On another occasion she referred to it as 'heaven' and 'a rest cure'.

The patients who interpret their illness as entirely physical find themselves in a situation where they too are mostly doomed to disappointment. They expect physical examinations and tests to pinpoint the cause of their troubles. They want physical treatments or medicine focused upon the part of the body which they believe to be disturbed. If they do not receive these they first feel anxious and then angry and bewildered. They complain that the doctor is inefficient and that they are not receiving treatment, or else they are receiving the wrong treatment. 'If only they could find out what makes that pendulum in my head, I'd be more satisfied.

Sometimes I think it's my eyes and then perhaps it's my blood pressure or my liver. Nothing seems to do any good.'

On the other hand, the young patients, who justify their illness by saying that it is caused by their background, are not only sure that the trouble is in their mind but anxious to receive psychotherapy which will enable them to 'sort it out'. They resent the hospital because they feel they receive too little attention. What they would really like is psychoanalytic treatment.

'I wasn't seeing anyone, I reckoned they'd forgotten about me,' said Mr. Jackson. 'I could have stayed there forever. I wasn't getting any further and I thought if I stayed there getting bored I might get like some of the others, so I came home.' These patients seem to try to be more aware of themselves than the patients in the other groups. Having tried hospital and been disappointed, they often return home to figure it out for themselves. They arrive at the same conclusion as the group who accept their illness—'it's mostly up to yourself'.

The patients who accept their illness do not display the extremes of feeling found among those who go to hospital with fantastic hopes or fantastic fears. They adopt an attitude of resigned co-operation towards the hospital. When they are not temporarily overwhelmed by a crisis, they are grateful for the help or shelter they receive, and extremely tolerant of the restrictions and regulations. Mr. Kerstein, for instance, besides patiently seeking a final understanding of his own illness, also educates other patients whom he meets both in the hospital and the community. He tries, too, to explain mental illness to non-patients, and modify their attitude to it.

But he himself realized the danger in resignation to hospital life: after a while it becomes more and more difficult to face the world again. 'The big danger for some is hospitalization. It's like a live bird—when you get a wild bird and put it in a cage and leave it for a few weeks, when

you open the door it doesn't want to fly away. You get
used to being inside, and when you come out everything's
strange.'

The danger is especially acute for those who seek a refuge
in hospital from their fears of everyday life. One woman,
who remained in hospital 3½ years, explained.

> 'I bet I'm the only one that ever put theirselves away. What
> do you think of that? I was frightened to go out and frightened
> to be alone. In the end I went and asked to go away. They
> didn't want me to, I put myself in there and I insisted until
> they let me go. Each time my husband came to visit me I used
> to say, "Don't ask me to come home because I couldn't enter-
> tain it." I needed to be somewhere that I felt safe, but I put
> myself behind bars to do it. If you stuck to the rules you were
> all right. In the end they shifted me everywhere about the
> hospital, according to where they wanted a bed. I didn't object
> too much as long as they let me stay there. We worked in
> together. I obliged them by moving and not making a nuisance
> of myself and they let me stay. I was very useful to them in that
> needle-room. I did a lot of work and I used to take messages
> all over the place too.'

She was a model patient as long as no one attempted to
treat her or send her home.

> 'I pretty soon worked out I didn't want any treatment. I don't
> believe in a lot of drugs and so on. When they came about
> treatments, Jane was missing, I can tell you. As he (the doctor)
> went into the day room I was making beds. When he was
> coming up to the ward I was nipping out with a message or
> fetching something from the kitchen. It was on account of
> him catching up with me that I decided to come home.'

So restrictions and routine which are intolerable to patients
who will not admit that they are ill, become protective
devices to others in flight from the world. By accepting all
manner of tasks in the hospital, they help to establish themselves there. They prefer a part in the routine to the hobbies
provided by the occupational therapist. As one woman
remarked, 'May be all right for those women from the

suburbs, but to take anyone from round our way and sit them down in front of a woolly dog is just silly, when they've been used to real work.'

The attitude to hospital experience is obviously directly linked with the expectation of what ought to happen in hospital. Whether hospital routine is seen as relevant or not depends upon the interpretation of the illness; if the patient feels he needs rest or physical treatment then chores are resented and psychotherapy resisted. If security is sought, chores are welcomed and if the illness is accepted, then co-operation is also forthcoming. If the illness is denied, co-operation is withheld at all levels.

The feelings of the patients' relatives follow a very similar pattern. They, too, are aware of the institutional character of the hospital. To them it is a place where people are 'put away', suitable only for lunatics. So they will only reluctantly take the initiative in admitting a member of their family to hospital, and defend themselves against accusations of heartlessness if they do.

> 'You don't like to put her away—what with her being a relative—but then the doctors found out for themselves how she was, and that was it. It was a neighbour who complained and called an ambulance at two o'clock in the morning.'

> 'We kept him back as long as we could, but in the end we had to let him go.'

So the relatives are as prejudiced about the hospital as the patients themselves. If the member of their family has been taken to hospital against their wishes, they will see only its grimmest aspects. If they have themselves arranged for his admission, they will ward off feelings of guilt by emphasizing its most cheerful features. And whether they initially accept or reject the hospital depends, too, on their closeness to the patient.

A woman who had never agreed to her husband's admission saw only the hospital gates, the patients in the grounds acting strangely, and was appalled by the visitor's hall.

Almost her first words to her husband on her first visit were 'You're not staying here. This is no place for you—it's terrible.' But the sister of another patient, glad to be relieved of her embarrassing presence at home, saw only the gardens. 'The flowers are so lovely, and the hospital looks so beautiful now it's been painted. All the nurses are kind, and so long as you aren't difficult, they put you in one of those nice villas. If you get in a bad ward where the patients frighten you, it's only a matter of pulling yourself together to get out.'

Just as there are patients who can be swayed by their experience of being in hospital into changing their original attitude, so after the admission of the patient the relatives may be impelled, by guilt or by shock at their first contact with hospital, to remove the patient, or agree to his return, in spite of a hostile or ambivalent feeling for him. The original decision to reject the responsibility for the patient is reversed and an uneasy time ensues in the patient's family. This was particularly true of the married men among the patients, where the wife had been torn between duty to the husband and to other members of the family.

Neither the patient nor his family, therefore, see the hospital simply as a means of providing treatment, any more than they see his abnormality simply as a disease. And the hospital is, indeed, more than a therapeutic centre. It is also a refuge for the helpless, and a means of protecting society against the irresponsible. At times its institutional severity seems to symbolize the hostility of society towards behaviour which it fears and cannot understand.

A fundamental dilemma underlies the position of a mental patient in society. In a normal person, his behaviour would be blamed as inept, irresponsible, even criminal. If he is not to be blamed and punished, it can only be because he is not accountable for his actions. But if he is not accountable, then he cannot be allowed to play a responsible part in society. He must be protected from his disabilities, and society must be protected from him: he loses his freedom.

So he is either to be condemned, or to be relieved both of the responsibilities and privileges of citizenship.

The attitude of the mentally ill, to their illness, to the hospital and to treatment depends, therefore, on how far they are willing to surrender their responsibilities. Once they admit that their judgement is deranged, they are likely to be dogged for the rest of their lives by disbelief and disparagement—you never know, you can't be too careful, it might happen again, better safe than sorry. It is therefore very difficult for them ever to recover their status. And while they are in hospital, they have to admit that the restrictions and routine which discount and devalue their individuality are justifiable: it would be absurd to run an institution to suit the convenience of aberrations. The mentally ill can only escape the condemnation of society by surrendering their freedom.

But the mentally ill not only fear the threat to their freedom from without: if they accept that they are not responsible for themselves, they must face the terrifying idea that they are being run by uncontrollable and unpredictable impulses. They are therefore under great pressure to evade such a painful issue. Their perception of their illness, of hospital, of their relationship to society are related by the way in which they reconcile these painful alternatives.

At one extreme is an attitude which uncompromisingly resists any attempt upon their freedom. The illness is denied: no treatment is needed. The hospital is a prison into which a mad or wicked world has thrust them. The determination to hold on to their right to run their own affairs forces them to see the world as their persecutor: since they are not ill, only malevolence can account for the way they have been treated.

Others are willing to accept that they are not altogether responsible for themselves, so long as they can feel that this is only a temporary derangement, thrust upon them by circumstances outside themselves which no one could have been expected to withstand. They feel that they are retreating from their responsibilities merely for a rest and treatment, as in any other sickness, and expect of the hospital sympathy and personal attention. They resent being made to work, the depersonalizing routine, the presence of other patients whom they consider, unlike themselves, to be mad. They resist the suggestion that their freedom is threatened from within, as well as by intolerable difficulties without: they are not abnormal, but merely overburdened, or physically unwell.

Others, again, prefer to surrender their freedom without qualification, for the sake of asylum from intolerable responsibilities. They try to acquire status within the hospital itself, co-operate willingly with the routine, and make themselves useful. But they evade treatment, since this threatens to return them to the outside world again.

Lastly, a few can bear to recognize the nature of their illness, and resign themselves to the routine of the hospital life from time to time, without losing their self-respect. They can do this because they set out to master their illness themselves; they become amateur psychiatrists, and, by an active responsibility for their own treatment, can compensate for their loss of status in the ordinary affairs of life. They identify themselves, in a sense, with the doctors. At the same time, they regard the hospital administration with the coolness of rivals.

The relatives of the mentally sick face similar problems. The more they care for the sick member of the family, the less easily can they admit that he is alienated from them by a fundamental abnormality, and the less willing they will be to surrender him to an institution. At the same time, they have to protect him against complaints of neighbours and other less committed relatives, and extricate him from the difficulties he may encounter. Sometimes they may identify themselves so closely that they accept his illusions or paranoid suspicions. But mostly they try to find a concept that will excuse his disabilities, without admitting that he is mentally ill, or that a mental hospital would be an appropriate place of treatment. They preserve the illusion that the sick are really responsible people by discharging many of their responsibilities on their behalf. They share the antipathy of many patients to hospital.

On the other hand, if the strain of caring for the patient becomes too much for them, they will see the hospital in a more attractive light. But in so far as they recognize a responsibility towards the sick man or woman, they are liable to feel guilty at acceding to his loss of freedom. Relatives who do not identify themselves so closely with the mentally ill are likely to perceive his illness sooner and more clearly, even brutally. They repudiate any responsibility for him, and justify themselves by emphasizing his incompetence to remain outside hospital. They may also wish to reassure themselves of their own normality, by dissociating themselves from him.[1]

The question of responsibility is therefore crucial, both for the patient and his family. If he is responsible, he is accountable, to blame. If he is not responsible, then he must be protected from himself, society from him: he loses his right to freedom and even to a hearing. And it is largely the way in which we conceive of mental illness through our laws and institutions which forces so harsh a choice. For we seem to find it very difficult to admit that a person may be partially responsible, able to meet some obligations for himself while needing to be relieved of others. In part, this is because we understand mental illness too little to distinguish with confidence between partial and total disablement. But in part it derives from the insensitivity of our

---

[1] A very similar set of attitudes has been noticed amongst members of the public who have some contact with mental patients. A study by Elaine and John Cumming describes 'first, denial of mental illness; second, isolation of the affected person in a hospital where mental illness can no longer be denied, with concomitant rationalization of this isolation with beliefs that the hospital is a wonderful place, capable of curing mental illness, if it can be cured at all, which is doubtful; and finally, insulation of the whole vexing problem by a secondary denial that a problem exists in so far as it needs solving by ordinary citizens'. Cumming, E. and J., *Closed Ranks*, pp. 122–3.

laws, and the character of the treatment which a mental patient receives. Our mental hospitals are still run,[1] from lack of staff, and for ease of administration, as if all patients were wholly irresponsible. They may be allowed to do little for themselves, robbed of their individuality, humiliated by the refusal of the staff to accept what they say or do as worth respect. By a curious logic, we try to equip people to resume their responsibilities by taking from them any responsibility whatever.

The family, as an informal group, can much more easily provide for a partially responsible member than an institution. It is more flexible, personal, and less exacting. But at present, treatment does not come into the home,[2] while the mentally ill and those who care for them are too afraid of the consequences to go in search of it.

---

[1] Even before the 1959 Act some hospitals permitted a large measure of freedom. Since the Act a growing number of hospitals have begun to allow the patients more initiative, but overcrowding and lack of staff coupled with custodial traditions continue to prevail in many hospitals.

[2] There are areas in which it does (e.g. Worthing and Nottingham) but in East London domiciliary visiting is the exception rather than the rule.

VI

KINSHIP AND MENTAL
ILLNESS

THE preceding chapters have described how patients came to hospital, how long they stayed and what were the attitudes of themselves and their relatives to their illness and its treatment. We have seen that from the patient's own point of view treatment was often difficult to accept, because they could not easily admit that their behaviour was disturbed. Many of the patients either rejected treatment or left before they were sufficiently well. But besides this, the institutional life of a hospital has practical disadvantages, and it is being increasingly recognized that an institution may not provide the best surroundings in which to treat at least the less severe cases. So there are in future likely to be more mentally sick people being cared for in their own homes. How far were the patients interviewed in this study cared for by their relatives at home, and what are the problems involved in enabling a mental patient to preserve some kind of independence in the community?

Since the patients were of both sexes, and ranged in age from 18 to 80 years, they differed very widely in their family circumstances. But compared with the general population of the borough, they included a high proportion of single people, especially amongst the young (Table IV).

Most of the younger male patients are single, compared with half of the equivalent group in the Survey Borough population. As many of the older men, on the other hand,

TABLE IV

SEX, AGE AND MARITAL STATUS OF PATIENTS COMPARED WITH POPULATION OF SURVEY BOROUGH*

Men	15–34		35–64		65+	
	Patients	*Borough Population*	*Patients*	*Borough Population*	*Patients*	*Borough Population*
Single	88%	50%	18%	14%	14%	10%
Married, Widowed or Separated ..	12%	50%	82%	86%	86%	90%
Total % ..	100%	100%	100%	100%	100%	100%
Number ..	16	8,664	17	10,313	7	2,460

Women	15–34		35–64		65+	
	Patients	*Borough Population*	*Patients*	*Borough Population*	*Patients*	*Borough Population*
Single	67%	43%	42%	16%	20%	9%
Married ..	33%	56%	33%	70%	20%	33%
Widowed or Separated ..	—	1%	25%	14%	60%	58%
Total % ..	100%	100%	100%	100%	100%	100%
Number ..	12	9,336	24	11,450	10	3,798

Notes: (i) Patients, 1956–57; Survey Borough Population, percentage distribution of those aged 15 or over at Census 1951.

(ii) Two women patients, aged 44 and 55, were separated.

* For further figures comparing the patients with the population of the Survey Borough, see Appendix 2.

are married as are men in the corresponding age group in the population of the borough. The women patients include more single people and fewer who were married, in all age groups. These differences may be characteristic of mental patients generally. The high proportion of young single men has been noted in several studies of mental illness. The peak age for the onset of schizophrenia is in the early 30's, while for the depressive illnesses it is much later. Schizophrenics are less often married than other patients. However, until the epidemiology of mental illness is more firmly established it is difficult to say whether the statistics derived from hospital admissions give a true reflection of the characteristics of the mentally ill as a whole. Family circumstances may make some people more liable to be admitted to hospital when they become mentally ill. This appears to be true, for instance, of the foreign-born patients in this survey. But since it is impossible to establish the age-distribution of the foreign-born in the area as a whole it is also impossible to exclude the possibility that this accounts for the high incidence of certain mental illnesses in particular age groups. The mentally ill who are isolated may enter hospital more frequently because they have no one to care for them. Yet isolation does not stand out unambiguously as a precipitating factor in hospital admission, for although some come to hospital after the loss of a particular relative who had cared for them, other patients seemed better able to avoid hospital because they were less closely involved with possessive relatives and outside the range of family quarrels.

The numbers in the present study are not large enough to justify any conclusions on these points, even if the necessary comparative data were available. Here nothing more is attempted than a description of the family circumstances of the patients.

The single patients

In the survey area children usually remain at home with their parents until marriage. Amongst the patients likewise only three of the 21 whose mother or father was still alive were apart from them. The three exceptions were all men. One had become a vagrant and two had been thrown out of their homes after the mother's death. Altogether 67% of the single patients had a mother still living, as many as would be expected from other studies in East London.[1]

The single patients were mostly devotedly cared for, even at the expense of other members of the family, so long as their mothers still lived. In general parents, and especially mothers, will make great sacrifices to keep their sick children at home. All but four of the single patients living with their parents were brought to hospital by someone outside the family, or through circumstances—such as an attempt at suicide—which were beyond their control. But though most young patients are cared for at home, their behaviour can put a great strain both on them and on the household in which they live. The devotion of one member can, for instance, provoke the jealousy of others.

The patient is rarely, if ever, treated alike by all members of his household, and they are affected in very varying ways by him. Often the patient becomes a focus for family conflicts in which some relatives seek to protect and make allowances for the patient while others complain of favouritism. This is particularly true where the patient lives with a group of siblings, and the mother seeks to defend and cherish the sick child to the detriment of the others. Mrs. Martin discussed this difficulty when describing her daughter Bella. 'She'll come in and I'll perhaps put her dinner down and she'll say, "I don't want that", and I'll say, "Oh, come on, dear, it's nice peas and mince", and she'll say, "I'm not eating it", and I get her something else —my boy Johnny gets mad and yells at her and the other girl gets cross too. I tell them to leave her alone because she's ill. But since I lost my husband I rely on Johnny's wages and he feels he has a right to get mad about throwing food away. He's jealous of Bella and flares up at her—I have to stand between them like.' Mrs. Wiles puts her schizophrenic son before her daughter's wish to bring home a boy friend. 'I tell them they'll have to explain as best they can.'

[1] The comparison is with a sample interviewed by Michael Young and Peter Willmott in 1956, as part of the study reported in *Family and Kinship in East London*.

Some of the mothers of single male patients took a sad pride in explaining that they had a special relationship with the mentally sick member of the family. Mrs. Wiles said, '*You* couldn't have a conversation with him, but I could. And then again, I don't want the others to know about him swearing in his room lately. *I* know that it will pass off, but they don't understand. When the children were younger he used to frighten them because they couldn't understand why he wasn't like them.' Mrs. Naughton liked to be left alone with her son, and they were happy when the rest of the family went out. The boy's father tried to make the interviewer become referee in family quarrels. Trying to escape from the situation, his wife had edged herself into a corner and turned her face to the wall and covered her ears. Mr. Naughton said, 'I tell her, she's not affectionate to me like she used to be. If I want a bit of cuddle, she doesn't want to know. . . .' Suddenly turning about, his wife blazed out at him unexpectedly, 'Oh, shut up!' and appealing to the interviewer, 'That just shows, men only want one thing, don't they?' Later, in the absence of the husband, she explained timidly, 'Tom (her sick son) is all right when he's with me. His brother and sister get niggled because he keeps fidgeting and shifting things about from here to there and his father tries to make him do things by shouting at him. It's no good to him, he's nervous like me. We like to sit quiet together on our own and watch the telly.'

Malcolm Hadfield's brother described him at first with considerable hostility, and later implied that he had tried to be tolerant and persuasive towards Malcolm, but since this had met with boorishness and unpleasantly bizarre behaviour, he now washed his hands of the whole business. His brother, he said, was obviously mad and hospital was the best place for him and for all concerned. During the course of the conversation he remarked, 'The trouble is my younger brother has always been spoiled ever since he was a child and now we're reaping the benefit.'

Mrs. Frohlich's mother explained how her daughter had always been difficult even as a child and the rest of the family had been irritated by her selfishness and by the fuss she made on the slightest pretext. 'Now she is ill they will not have her in their homes. They said it is not right or fair to their children, even when the children are big. Why should they have her when she has always been selfish? I have to leave my comfortable home and come here to this terrible place. The others sometimes come here, but only to visit me, they do not come to see her. If she does not try to be better before I die what will become of her? She will have no one. I have to go on living because I am her mother.'

The situation in another family shows how Mrs. Frohlich's fears might well be confirmed. On the death of the parents one daughter was left to cope with her mentally sick sister, of whom she had been jealous since childhood because of the special attention the sister had received. She was often driven to the limits of her endurance by her sick sister's behaviour, but even when she felt most hostile she bought the patient a television set, and she wept when she described the patient's state of mind. When she asked for her sister to be certified she suffered from feelings of guilt and remorse. After the patient's admission she did not at first visit her, and prevented others from doing so, but suddenly began to visit and take presents. Eventually she allowed the patient to return home. She was visibly torn between hatred and guilt.

In several households, the difficulties were increased because more than one of the children was mentally ill. It is then almost impossible to prevent all of them from going into hospital. Mrs. Guarita came from a peasant community in Russia and after surviving the revolution with two small children she brought them on seven different trains across Europe to find her husband, who had escaped to London earlier during the fighting. They settled in the East End like many of their friends, and had some more children.

As they grew up the eldest son, who had been brought to England as a toddler, became schizophrenic. His mother kept him at home for seven years, but he was an incurable wanderer and she could not keep him indoors. Finally, when her youngest daughter became mentally disturbed Mrs. Guarita arranged for the eldest son to go to hospital, where he has remained. The daughter Nella was nursed and cared for at home until the younger son became a depressive patient. Nella developed screaming fits and Mrs. Guarita was approached by the neighbours very sympathetically, but they said they could stand the screaming in the tenement no longer. Unable to take her young son to the out-patient clinic while leaving Nella unattended, she took to her bed in a state of collapse and allowed Nella to be taken to hospital. As soon as the daughter's crisis was over she fetched her home again. But her secret favourite is the younger son. She guards him from every difficulty and encourages him in every aspect of his career.

The evidence of the present study suggests that the relationship of the mother with a sick son tends to be closer than with a sick daughter. The mother of one woman patient, for instance, had rejected her since early childhood, and she had been brought up by a grandmother. Another clearly preferred her son, who was not ill, and resented her daughter's tantrums. She said rather bitterly, 'When Ruth was getting some of her queer ideas she'd sit there as if she didn't know what was going on and talk to herself, but she always knew what I'd said if I offered her a pound.'

The mothers of the men patients never showed this kind of resentment. Only twice was a special relationship between the mentally ill daughter and her father observed, which appeared to be akin to the tie between the single male patients and their mothers. Mr. Lucas persisted in the belief that his schizophrenic daughter was 'run down' even in the face of her open abuse and ridicule and bizarre hallucinations. In his opinion 'a few weeks in the country' and return to a light job at home was all that was necessary.

He continued to smile at her tenderly when she humiliated him in front of strangers. Similarly, Alice Meier's father stirred up bitter jealousy amongst his children by favouring the patient. Her sister said bitterly, 'She's only having to weep on Papa's shoulder and he's giving in to her already.' But neither Mr. Lucas nor Mr. Meier could keep their daughters out of hospital for ever.

Sometimes the relationship between parent and child seemed morbid in its intensity. Other studies have suggested that young men who suffer from schizophrenia are often dominated by abnormally possessive mothers; and this possessiveness may keep them out of hospital for a long time when they are very obviously ill, perhaps aggravating their illness. At all events, it seems often to protect the patient at the expense of other members of the household. Once the mother is dead, nobody else is likely to have the same concern for the patient, and they will more often find themselves alone. One young patient, for instance, lost his mother the day before he was due for discharge from hospital. He had made good progress and was looking forward to going home. But although his mother died four years ago, he is still in hospital; his father is fond of him, but has not the same compulsion to have him at home.

Single people, therefore, seem to depend very much on their parents, and especially on their mothers. The experience of Paul Golinsky illustrates how they may become completely isolated after the mother's death. Paul first experienced mental disturbance consciously at the age of nine when his father, reproached by an invalid wife for 'carrying on' with other women while she was bedridden, flew into a temper and lunged at the sick woman and struck her. The mother was only too aware of the close tie between herself and her son and of the fact that she alone in the household was prepared to bear the burden of his illness. As she lay dying, when Paul was about 13, she said to him, 'What will become of you when I'm gone? You'll have no one when I've gone.' When he was 15 Paul went into lodgings and has lived alone ever since. He lives in one room with a half dozen possessions to his name, pinning his hopes on the pools.

Few patients are so completely rejected by their families. John Mace, for instance, was cared for by a married sister until her husband objected. John's mother had an illness during pregnancy and John was born physically abnormal. His mental troubles developed later. When the father and some of the siblings could no longer tolerate John, his mother left home with him, and they were joined by John's younger sister. When the mother died John went to hospital for the first time, just as Paul went to hospital first after the death of his mother. John's younger sister married, but continued to help her brother until her husband insisted that their connexion with John should cease. 'My little boy,' he explained, 'is beginning to imitate what John does and how he talks and he gets frightened of him sometimes too. And another thing, if you give John a pound today he'll be back tomorrow without a penny in his pocket. He loses it or gives it away or he buys them drinks round the pub.' John's father and older siblings who have more money and no small children will have nothing to do with him. Since his mother's death he has no home and no one to stand by him. When he is not in hospital he lives a one-roomed, meals-on-a-gas-ring existence.

More often brothers and sisters are ready to admit some responsibility, even though they will not accept the patient into their own household. Mrs. Abel insisted that she had done all she could for her brother, Thomas, and that it was impossible for her to have him in her home, 'because the accommodation goes with the job. I've worked with this firm for more than 20 years, I'll be due to retire soon and I don't want to spoil it all now. I would have him, but the firm would never allow it.' She blamed another sibling whom she described as 'a free agent' for refusing to live with Thomas. Mr. Mackirdy's brother, on the other hand, although maintaining a sense of duty towards the patient, was not even interested in lessening the distance between his home and his brother's lodgings. Mr. Mackirdy himself was aware of this, 'I've worn my welcome out there,' he explained, without bitterness.

Sometimes the patient's relatives, after giving him a home on the death of his mother, later arranged for him to live near them, but not with them. Henry Higgs' family had spent more than 20 years passing him from one household in the family to the next and finally had taken a single room for him almost next door to a sister, who kept his room clean and undertook the care of his laundry and mending. He often has a meal with her, but they are never together for long and in this way she finds they can live side by side, though she found she could not endure the anxiety of his permanent presence under her roof.

Miss Ann Dove was brought up by her father's sister because her own mother went into a mental hospital while still quite young. Ann's cousins married, but she remained at home with her aunt and uncle and cared for them till their death. Her aunt's eldest daughter now accepts responsibility for Ann, since she has become mentally disturbed. Although this eldest cousin, Mrs. Rudd, is rather indifferent to Ann Dove, she does keep contact with her and has her to meals at the weekend. The other cousins help to decorate her flat and assist in similar ways, but they are all unwilling to take her into their household permanently. In moments of great crisis Mrs. Rudd appeals to Ann's brothers and for the time being they respond, but Ann soon returns to Mrs. Rudd's doorstep.

Similarly, Miss Katie Paul, an elderly spinster patient, lives near, not with, her widowed sister. The sister, Mrs. Eaton, said, 'I pop down to her flat almost every day and see that she's keeping things going, otherwise she slips back into doing nothing. I don't have room for her up here, and it's better for her to manage for herself. It gives her something to do and keeps her mind off her aches and pains.'

As the three preceding illustrations show, in some

respects the mentally sick may be more likely to manage better if they live near their relatives than with them. They can still be helped with meals and housework, while they do not have the strain of adapting themselves to a normal household, and the patience of their relatives is not taxed at every hour of the day by their strange behaviour. But the position of any sick person on his own in society is bound to be precarious.

Although most of the single patients lived with their parents, and some of the others had relatives near them, in Britain as a whole the proportion of mental patients who live alone is almost certainly greater than appears from the present study. Unlike the adjoining areas, the survey borough has no Rowton Houses, or Salvation Army hostels, and few places where the isolated wanderer can find cheap lodgings. Many of the single men are therefore likely to drift away. Malcolm Hadfield, for instance, became a vagrant after a series of disastrous quarrels with his family. When not scraping an existence on the bomb-sites and in the cafés of the area, Malcolm disappeared to cheap lodgings in London near the large railway termini, where he joined a group of mentally disturbed friends who came from all parts of the world. Though many originated in Ireland, other parts of London, or large provincial cities, some belonged to the East End, like Malcolm himself. Sometimes he could not afford even the shared room in town and came to a Rowton House or men's hostel in one of the adjacent boroughs. Judging from the experience of several of the young single men, it seems likely that more mentally ill men leave the borough than are drawn into it. This would not be so for single women, if only because there are fewer women's hostels. Perhaps too, mentally disturbed women are more often accepted as a family responsibility, because they are considered more vulnerable.[1]

---

[1] Only a quarter of the single women in the sample lived alone, and all but one was over 60: half the single men lived alone, and they were younger. But the numbers are too small to draw any conclusions.

The widowed and divorced

Amongst those who have never married, isolation does not seem much to affect the likelihood of their admission to hospital. Most of these single patients still have parents alive, willing to make sacrifices for their care. It may, however, have more influence on the admission of older, widowed people.[1] There were only 14 widowed, separated or divorced patients in the sample—all but two of them women—so the numbers are too few to draw any conclusions. But more of them lived alone, and fewer had children, than would be expected amongst widowed and divorced people of their ages. Only 12% of the women lived with an adult child, compared with 45% of widowed and divorced or separated women in the borough as a whole; 41% as against 20% had no children over the age of 18; and 63% as against 41% lived alone.

Even when there are children at hand to help, their responsibilities towards their husbands or wives and their own children limit the sacrifices they can make for their parents. Mrs. Jackson, for instance, found herself torn between the needs of her husband and children, and those of her elderly mother, Mrs. Brenner. The mother was admitted to hospital after a struggle which lasted five years; her daughter Mrs. Jackson said, 'Sometimes I've felt so upset about leaving her there. We didn't like having to do it, but what was there to be done? There was nothing to be done about it at all. We'd all got our own problems and we've all got to go out to work. If I don't work who's going to keep my family? I've got nobody to earn money for me. My husband's a sick man and I have to earn for both of us.' Later in the conversation she reiterated that if it had not been for her sick husband she would 'never have allowed mother to go to hospital'.

[1] See Titmuss, R. M., and Abel-Smith, B., *The Cost of the National Health Service in England and Wales*, pp. 140–6. This question is further discussed in Appendix 3, pp. 175–177.

The married women

Fewer married women come to Long Grove from the survey area than any other group. For one thing, the routine of their home depends on them so much—especially if they have children—that the greatest efforts will be made to enable them to remain there. The wives who do come are usually not native to the borough and so have less relatives at hand to help them. Mr. Valdar, the husband of one of the young foreign-born patients, put this point very clearly in his attempt to explain the situation. 'When the man gets sick the woman is not having such a bad time as the man when the mother goes to hospital. I had to put my son with friends, I was working on shifts, looking after myself and the house and visiting my wife at Epsom and my son in another part of London. When the man goes, the woman and children stay at home and only have to visit the man on top of their usual work.' The married women with children are therefore most needed.[1] At the same time, they can be cared for at home, provided they have female relatives who are available to merge some of the mentally sick woman's work with their own.

A wife who suffers from mental illness is likely to need as much help from her relatives as a single woman, since her husband will be out at work all day, and she may have children as well as herself to care for. In the survey borough generally, the tie between mother and daughter remains close after the daughter's marriage: the young wife sets up home with, or near, her mother, and they help each other out in caring for the children, shopping, and housework. So the married women who suffer from mental illness may be more likely to enter hospital, if their mother is dead or living at a distance. In fact, only seven of the married women in the

---

[1] The balance between the advantage and disadvantage of the sick wife and mother remaining at home is very precarious, but her very presence often suffices to keep the family together. The actual presence of the father is not essential in the same way.

sample had mothers alive and of these seven, five lived 50 miles or more apart, one 20 miles, and only one lived with her mother. Two had left their mothers in another country. The day-to-day shopping expeditions with Mum, the friendly chat, her advice in moments of crisis, had no part in the daily lives of the married women patients.

Mrs. Mayerat was separated from her parents at the age of ten and reunited with them at the age of 18, but they both died before her marriage. Mrs. Moeller's mother lives out in the country and comes up to see her daughter and grand-children about once a month. The family history is one of erratic movement from one end of England to the other. 'We never had a fixed home,' said Mrs. Moeller, 'it's what I want for my own children.' Mrs. Chidley's mother, on the other hand, had moved only once and that was away into Essex, leaving her daughter in East London. Mrs. Chidley's sister moved with the mother and they seem to be absorbed in voluntary work so that they do not come to see Mrs. Chidley as often as they could. The sister was calling the day following the interview, but the mother had decided to attend a meeting in connexion with a committee instead.

The married women patients as a whole tend to be 'strangers' to the neighbourhood. Almost half of all the married women were born in another country and very few were born in the borough. Mrs. Bohm's mother lived in Warsaw, where she remained when her daughter was cap-tured and taken to a prison camp in Germany, later to be released by the British and transferred to the Polish forces in Britain. Mrs. Bohm's only surviving brother came to England after the war, but following a painful family quarrel he ceased visiting her. Her mother's infrequent letters are the only link she has with the family into which she was born. The proportion of married women patients born outside the borough is considerably greater than would be expected when compared with a group of similar age taken from the population of the borough—87% instead of 46%.

Married men

The married men amongst the patients were not similarly isolated. Three-quarters were born in the borough or an adjoining borough, and all but one—who came from abroad —were born in London. They had, as a whole, as many relatives, and lived as near them, as most men in this area. They were admitted to hospital, not because they lacked relatives themselves, but rather because their wives lacked relatives to help in caring for them. For both married women and married men, it is the absence of available women relatives on the wife's side that is significant.

In this community a man tends to be drawn into his wife's family much more than she is drawn into his. He sees more of her relatives than his own, and it is to her own family, not his, that his wife will turn for help—especially to the women of her family. But among the 20 wives of the men in the sample, only two had women relatives at hand to help them. For the rest, their relatives, if they had any, either lived too far away or were unable to help because of sickness or other responsibilities.

Mrs. Atterbury lost her parents when she was a child; she had no brothers or sisters; her son died in childhood and one of her two daughters went to live in South Africa.

Mrs. Borland's mother is dead, and she has only one sister. 'There was always just the two of us, then my sister married and went to live in Gloucestershire.'

Mrs. Churchley's mother lived in the next block of flats, but she is an elderly invalid, and only an added responsibility to her daughter, already over-burdened with worry and distress. Mrs. Churchley had recently moved, and knew none of the neighbours, and sometimes scarcely saw them for weeks on end, while her other relatives had 'moved on down the line'— to Dagenham, Hainault and Debden. So she had no one to turn to for help.

Mrs. Frank Texter had no help from women relatives at the time of her husband's illness. Her mother is dead, one of her sisters is dead, another 'became a religious and it's ten years ago that I last saw her'. The only other sister is married and does in fact live at the other end of an adjacent borough, but this sister is tied to the house with four small children and, therefore, can be of little help to Mrs. Texter during times of crisis. She faced, single-handed, a mountain of problems which would daunt most women even with the help of mothers and sisters. The housing conditions in her area are appalling, she herself has had pneumonia, one child was in hospital, another sickly and finally her husband had a mental collapse. Because of the debt accumulated during his stay in hospital she had to continue her part-time job as a cleaner, even though it meant leaving a sick child in the house alone.

Even though they had so few relatives to whom they could turn for help, only four of the wives willingly agreed to their husband's admission to hospital. Seven were forced to accept it through circumstances beyond their control— a clash with the police, attempted suicide, or because their husbands were referred for psychiatric treatment from a general hospital. The remainder struggled sometimes ten or 15 years with great difficulties until the problems became too great for them. Even when their husband became violent, they did not seek to have him admitted to hospital, unless the children were threatened.

Marriage and mental illness[1]

In four instances, the wives themselves also suffered from mental illness. It seems likely that people who are mentally ill, if they marry, tend to choose partners who are also ill more often than might be expected by chance, and that it is not always the most sick partner who is finally admitted to hospital. There is probably a mutual attraction between men and women who face the same problem in accepting the world in which they live. And in any case, their disabilities may make it difficult for them to find a man or woman who will take them. Finding a suitable wife is

[1] See Ødegård, Ø, 'New Data on Marriage and Mental Disease. The incidence of Psychoses in the widowed and divorced'.

particularly difficult for the son who remains at home to support a widowed mother.[1] If he has developed mental illness the situation is infinitely more complicated. He may be emotionally and financially tied to her. When she dies he is past the normal marriage age and the majority of the women of his own generation are now married. He is forced to choose a wife from the widowed, from women of his own age who have previously been rejected, or from the group of women much younger than himself who are about to get married. Under these circumstances he is more likely to marry a woman who is emotionally disturbed, and due to the stress of his own past he may not easily adapt to her difficulties or she to his. Moreover, if there is a wide age-gap between them, one of their children will be left with a widowed parent and may repeat the pattern followed by the father.

Sometimes parents may arrange a match for their sick children to relieve their own responsibilities. One of the patients, for instance, had made friends with a girl while they were both in hospital. After they had both returned home, her mother deliberately encouraged the acquaintance, and succeeded in arranging their marriage. Thereafter she lived with her daughter and son-in-law, who in spite of his illness supported them both. Occasionally he gave way to violence under the strain. 'It's a funny thing,' the old lady remarked, 'whenever he's in one of his moods, it's always me he goes for.' In another instance a wealthy father hoped to use his money to find a wife for his son. 'He's had cars, clothes, money, and everything he wanted,' Mr. Goldschmidt said, 'I'd sooner be in prison than watch this boy day and night. When I'm home I'm a warder, and I've got it with me all day long.' What would save Gerald was marriage with an older woman, he thought. A girl would be interested in a younger man with money and prospects, 'even if he was a bit nutty'. What he wanted was someone older who was on the shelf and would be a good 'driver'

[1] For further discussion of this point see Appendix 3, pp. 175-177.

for Gerald, he explained. 'A girl getting Gerald would be getting a good bargain,' he added. But such a marriage might well create more problems for his sick son than it solved.

We have seen that most of the patients were, wholly or partly, cared for by their families and lived either with them or near them. But at what cost does a family continue to care for a mentally sick relative? How great are the difficulties facing the patient who tries to remain outside hospital? Is the sick man always a burden to his family or has the responsibility for an over-dependent family made him sick?

VII

LIFE AT HOME

O N the whole, whether they were single, married, or
widowed, most of the patients were cared for by
members of their family. Many of them were able
to take an active part in their family affairs, while others
could be entrusted with very little.

Mrs. Bohm, for instance, organized her household with considerable skill and took great trouble to extend the education
of her children. She not only solved many of the very serious
problems facing this little immigrant family, but also took in
outwork to help the family finances as well as running her
home and caring for the children. The family revolved around
her and she appeared to make the major decisions for all of
them. They were lost without her when she went to hospital.

Mrs. Gathercole's way of life offers a complete contrast. She
belongs to a family reduced to a mere handful by death and
disaster. She is fully absorbed into the family because all the
attention of her female relatives (there are only two men left
in the entire family) is centred upon her. They tend her like a
small child and defend her from the outside world. She goes
alone to her local doctor and almost every day she walks alone
in the park. Apart from this she sits and looks at newspapers
for an hour or two and occasionally, her aunt says, she wipes
a duster over the furniture with slow purposeless movements.
Every activity is a long and arduous process. She does as she
is told and is washed, fed and dressed by her relatives. They
arrange their entire life around her needs. They are all elderly
and retired.

Between these extremes are patients who had few

responsibilities, but were able for the most part to look after themselves.

Mr. Borland also lives with his family, but he does not share many activities with them. He observes, every day, a precise routine of his own. He walks two miles every morning to a seat in a park, and after sitting there for exactly the same time each day, he returns. Sometimes he makes a few purchases, carefully comparing prices in the market, or pauses to pick up discarded bits and pieces which may come in useful. Only occasionally is this routine broken, when he goes to the cinema with his family or helps with the shopping.

Mr. Higgs, too, has his own routine. But though he lives alone his life is in some ways less separate from his family. He calls on one sister every day and often has a hot meal with her. He brings her his washing and tells her how his pet cats and birds in the neighbourhood are getting on. He is very fond of children and animals, but shy of adults unless they belong to his own small group in the park. He visits another sister once a week when his work makes it convenient. Every day he spends some time in the same corner of a public garden with his cronies. They talk about their symptoms, their financial problems, politics and horses. He talks very little to anyone else.

As a whole, the mental patients were not simply a liability to their relatives. But nearly all of them, in one way or another, caused anxiety. Apart from fits of violence or attempts on their own life, some strained to the limit the patience of their households by their everyday behaviour.

More than half the patients were difficult at home—they quarrelled over meals; had phobias about food; expected to be waited on hand and foot; would occupy the bathroom for hours on end because they were obsessed with fears of contamination. Some were unable to wash and dress themselves, or were unwilling or extremely forgetful. A few were incontinent. 'You always know when he's getting bad because he lets himself go.'

Many of the relatives also complained of disturbed nights. Patients who were apathetic and almost immobile by day often became noisy and violent by night or had an incurable habit of wandering about. Other patients had the habit of sitting up and making up huge fires which terrified the family for fear of the house being burnt down. The wife of one said, 'I keep getting up and looking over the head of the stairs for fear he's set the place alight. He says it's night time that they'll get him so he must keep awake to catch them. I don't ever get my proper rest.' And the sister of another, 'She locks herself in and piles the fire up with coal. I can hear it roaring and I get frightened. She won't let me in and I'm afraid to go to bed.'

But those practical problems on the whole caused less strain than the strange fancies or dumb apathy from which some of the patients suffered in crises of their illness. It is difficult to imagine the degree of suffering caused by excessive silence or excessive speech. Someone has called the small recurrent vexations and difficulties, 'the martyrdom of the strong'. Many relatives complained that at one phase or another of their illness the patient persistently talked to themselves—'she talks and talks and nods at the walls all the time'; 'he has the laughing habit. Suddenly he'll laugh all to himself'; 'she raved and raved and when she was very bad she would fling up the window and swear something terrible at the people going by'. Some talked to themselves in an incessant undertone, or described their terrifying hallucinations—'She's lost her lungs. She ought not to have told me a thing like that. There's blood everywhere'. One woman kept up a continuous fretting conversation, 'I can't do without the drugs, but they make me feel worse. My skin's gone all creased, it's the drugs. There's something wrong in my mind. I'm sure I shall go mad. I keep wanting to throw myself under a bus. I get dizzy. There's something wrong with my stomach, do you think it could be cancer?' Her sister said, 'Sometimes when she stands behind me while I'm working and goes on like that I begin to feel so ill I say to her, "Iris, go upstairs and shut the door, if you don't go away from me I shall scream".'

But the relatives of patients who do not speak are often more distressed than those just described. 'You can't get a word out of Vincent now—sometimes he won't speak all evening and sometimes not much in a week,' said one father, and a wife fretted because her husband rarely speaks to her—'There's no life in him like there used to be'. In a depressive phase, some patients will stare at the wall, unseeing and silent for a week at a time, if nobody forces them out of their apathy. They give the impression of a dumb man learning to speak, or a man returning very slowly to consciousness. A monosyllable will be followed after many signs and an interval of several minutes, which seem an eternity, by two words or another monosyllable.

Apart from the distress they caused to their households, they sometimes greatly restricted the social life of the other members because they were too timid to go out themselves, or were afraid of strangers in the house. They might also antagonize their neighbours—by paranoid suspicions about them, screaming fits or shouted obscenities—and their relatives could not always protect them from the complaints which arose from such behaviour.

A few, too, were not safe with money—they would lose it, throw it or give it away, or object on principle to obtaining the pension or assistance to which they were entitled. One or two exhausted their resources in order to hoard possessions. The landlady of one young man who went to hospital described how he 'developed the habit of buying bikes. Eventually he graduated to two brand new special bikes which he was always cleaning and mending. Those bikes seemed to be everything which he hadn't had as a child, to him. But he also laid great store by having *two* television sets. Having one of anything didn't seem to be enough for him. Then he got the hoarding habit. When the man came from the welfare department at County Hall we went through every scrap of thousands of pieces of paper because nobody knew anything about him. Then there were immense piles of rubbish which he had hidden away in strange places. I couldn't believe it when we opened all the cupboards. He'd hidden food away in scraps too. But his money was tied up in bundles in an old shopping bag.'

For all these reasons, the patients could only survive as members of society because someone was willing to make sacrifices to help them in their difficulties. Table V sets out how often various kinds of difficulty arose.

TABLE V

DIFFICULTIES FOR THE FAMILY (NUMBER OF PATIENTS, OF THE 86, CAUSING VARIOUS DIFFICULTIES)

	Per-sistent	Inter-mittent	Very occasional	Total
Difficult behaviour in the family	19	21	8	48
Dangerous to self and others	15	20	10	45
Difficult behaviour in the neighbourhood	10	17	4	31
Silent or very talkative	11	14	3	28
Not helpful in the house	15	4	6	25
Troublesome at night	10	10	2	22
Supervision needed for washing, dressing	11	6	4	21
Would not get out or meet people at home	6	7	5	18
Not safe with money	7	7	3	17
Food problems	8	4	3	15
Housebound	6	3	1	10
Laundry problems due to incontinence	7	2	0	9

Very few patients caused difficulty in all of these ways, but only ten of the 86 are not represented in this list.

Most of the patients therefore needed some protection from their own disabilities and made at times exacting demands upon those who cared for them. In spite of the great sacrifices sometimes involved, relatives did accept these burdens. Because of this the patients with strong kinship ties in the borough could often stay out of hospital longer than the isolated. This is illustrated by the fact that people born in the borough had, on average, been mentally ill for six years before their first admission to hospital, compared with two years for those born outside it. Furthermore when they were admitted, the locally-born people tended to stay in hospital longer, as Table VI shows.

TABLE VI

LENGTH OF STAY IN HOSPITAL—PATIENTS BORN IN SURVEY
BOROUGH COMPARED WITH THOSE BORN OUTSIDE IT

Length of Stay in Hospital	*Patients born*	
	In the Borough	*Elsewhere*
One year or over	40%	7%
Repeated admissions within one year ..	38%	36%
One week to one year (admitted once only)	9%	39%
Less than one week	13%	18%
Total %	100%	100%
Number	48	38

There seems no doubt that this difference is due to the fact that the locally born patients were more seriously ill when they went to hospital. Only on one point, that of supervision for their own safety, did the others exceed the locally-born patients in the severity of their disturbances. Moreover, a much higher proportion of the locally-born were brought to hospital by people other than the family. More than half the patients born in the borough, but only a quarter of the others, were admitted to hospital because of the intervention of the police, a social worker, the neighbours or on the insistence of the G.P. Those patients who were locally born, and were admitted by request of a relative, were very seriously ill indeed. In one case the patient used to throw boiling water and knives at her sister, who endured a nerve-racking life for several years before she asked her doctor to arrange certification. The family were deeply shocked by the patient's admission and were still very ambivalent and guilty about it many months after.

Not all the remaining locally-born patients were violent, but they were all seriously ill, and had been for some time when they were first admitted. It may seem perverse in the face of these facts and figures to suggest that the mentally disturbed who are born in the area are not, on the whole, much sicker than patients admitted from the borough but originating elsewhere. The argument, however, is that the locally-born patients seen in the hospital form the third of the iceberg which shows above the surface, while the other two-thirds remain unnoticed within an extended kinship group at home. Those in hospital therefore present an exaggerated picture of the native person's mental illness. It is striking that none of the locally-born patients who come from a typical family are admitted to hospital with mild forms of illness. The locally-born patients, it seems, tend to be so closely interwoven with their families, and their attachment to the community to be so strong, that they are cared for in the community until their condition becomes severe.

In extreme contrast to this integration is the foreign-born person whose desire to establish attachments in the local community is ambivalent. The immigrant who is mentally disturbed finds the constant pressure of new challenges bewildering and exhausting. The homes of these immigrant patients reflect the culture from which they have been separated as well as a tentative reaching out towards the least strange elements in the new.

In one house a couple had bought articles in the local street market and combined them with a few remnants from Lithuania and the Ukraine in a manner which made the house totally foreign to the locality. Vivid wallpaper, where red and white cockatoos flew through a jungle of emerald green, sprang at the eye with a blaze of colour. On the table a cloth, brought from Birmingham by an Indian trader, argued in colour and texture with velvet cushions, on which wide-eyed Persian cats were painted. The flag of the Ukraine hung next to the wall plaque of the Madonna, and the stern face of a political leader looked across at the family pictures grouped around a miniature shrine and candle; the pictures were of a peasant farmer and his wife who died in a labour camp which the patient had survived. This was not Lithuania, not Russia, but not East London. This patient shared a problem with other immigrants; she had come from a country which no longer exists in the form in which she knew it and emotionally she belongs nowhere.

Often they retreated into fantasies. One man insisted on packing to be ready to take the next boat to the country where he was born; a woman believed that the people in the area were all conspiring against her. Another woman explained how much easier it was for her to live in the hospital because she had spent her adolescence in a labour camp. 'For these other people it is difficult, but for me to be in a dormitory with many other people, it is easy. If you have lived in the prison camps a mental hospital is clean and warm and comfortable. The regulations are very light and the closeness of people who behave strangely is easy not to notice.' She had learnt to live quietly within herself under such circumstances, and hospital routine was more familiar and tolerable to her than the social life of East London. Although some of these immigrant patients have children to draw them into the community, their connexions with the local people are extremely slight and fragile. Such people come to hospital rather easily: they accounted for 12% of the patients—three times the proportion that would be expected.[1] But since most immigrant families are small and

---

[1] Foreign-born immigrants are not necessarily evenly distributed in the population by age. People may be more likely to leave their native country at certain ages. Again, there are waves of immigrants at times of political persecution. Thus there may be a higher proportion of immigrants in particular age groups and those

isolated, they are desperately missed while in hospital and they are taken home again as soon as circumstances and the slender resources of their family permit.

It seems likely that immigrant families form a disproportionate number of mental hospital patients and some of these at least need not have entered hospital for treatment if they had been less isolated in the communities where they lived. They often need a special kind of help to enable them to adapt to an alien culture.

Patients in hardship

So far this chapter has described the family circumstances of the mental patients. They show how important the family was in protecting them within the community, and what burdens were sometimes accepted. Sometimes indeed the patients may have been over-protected, especially the young single men. Some of the patients with the strongest ties in the community seem to have been kept out of hospital until they had reached a state of regression in which they may need much physical as well as mental nursing. By then the prospects of treatment were much poorer. Their families might have surrendered them more readily but for the strong prejudice against institutional care.

The chances of such patients accepting treatment in time would probably be greater if it were available to them while they still lived at home. But if they are more often to be treated from their own homes, then their families should not have to bear without help the severe practical problems and strains. Some relatives need relief from the patient part

---

might happen to coincide with age peaks for mental illness. However, this does not affect the different proportions between the mental patients and the local population here given, since they have been matched for age and sex. Though larger numbers would be needed to confirm it, there seems to be an association between foreign birth and risk of becoming a mental patient. (Foreign born 1 in 79: British born 1 in 250.) Probably isolation and the difficulties of adjusting to a strange culture have much to do with it. But it is also possible that the mentally disturbed are more likely to emigrate from their country of origin than the better adjusted. See Malzberg, B., and Lee, E. S., *Migration and Mental Disease*.

of each day, others at night, some only during crisis periods. In some cases it may be better to help the patient to be more independent of his family while still living near them. The experience of the patients interviewed suggests that at present they only remain in the community at the cost of considerable hardship.

Some patients endure much physical hardship in addition to their mental stress. One young man provides an extreme illustration. His face and body are emaciated by long-term malnutrition; his shoulders droop and his dark clothes hang on his bony frame. The skin stretches tightly over the bones of his face, the cheeks are hollow, the grey eyes stare, sometimes with piercing intensity when the face is flushed with resentment, but more often blankly with bleak and familiar sadness. The room which he occupies is 8 by 6 feet, with a sharply sloping ceiling under the pitch of the roof. The small window with its decaying frame looks out on to a narrow bricked yard and the wall of another house. The room is clean and orderly though the fireplace is crumbling and the walls lean drunkenly in different directions. There are two chairs and a small table, an oil stove for warmth and cooking. A roll of three blankets wound round a pillow lies on top of a large suitcase. There is no bed, no cupboard, no chest of drawers. He sleeps in the chair or stretched on the floor. Two string lines carry the washing and his ward-robe. A kettle, a saucepan, frying-pan, two plates, knife, fork, spoon, a jug and a cup complete his possessions. Above the mantelshelf hangs the only decoration; the portrait of a woman resistance leader. 'Most blokes go for pin-ups, but she sort of gives me courage,' he explained.

Twelve of the 86 patients lived like this on the edge of destitution. Three of them had no regular work or fixed address: sometimes they lived on National Assistance, or worked as labourers or road sweepers, but for the most part they scraped a living busking, begging rags, and cadging food, shelter and drinks. Sometimes working, sometimes wandering, now able to sustain life in one room, cooking on a gas ring, now falling into phases of violent and aimless vagrancy, they were in the final stage of attachment to society. Beyond them live the truly destitute—the tramps, the homeless, the methylated-spirit drinkers—sleeping on bombed sites, under bridges or in any of a hundred holes and corners of East London.

Most of the other nine very poor patients lived a harsh one-roomed life, while two lived on the fringe of an impoverished family which gave them a roof over their head, cast-off clothing, an irregular diet and little more. Five lived on National Assistance and had done so for a long time. Two had old-age pensions and the remainder alternated fitfully between employment, assistance and 'getting by'. They had either had no chance to build up savings and possessions because they had never been regularly employed, or their resources had been exhausted by long years of hospital life, illness at home and the grinding struggle to keep going in the face of continuing financial responsibilities and diminishing income. During the most serious periods of disturbance outside hospital, many were unable to use their slender finances to the best advantage. Since these patients are only fitfully employed they may have insufficient stamps to qualify for unemployment or sickness benefit, or soon exhaust their benefit. They must then turn to the National Assistance Board for help. But some were either too confused to set about obtaining money to which they were entitled, or they objected on principle or were totally indifferent to National Assistance.

Beside the 12 already mentioned, a further 36 patients only managed with difficulty to secure more than the basic necessities of life. However, while their lives were never very secure, the patients and families in this group seemed quite certain that they belonged to society in general; they did not see themselves as outcasts, nor imagine that they would become 'down and out'. Among the almost destitute patients there were men who, in moments of depression or fear, would say, 'I'm on the way to the churchyard', meaning a bombed church in a neighbouring borough which is the camping ground of the tramps and the men who have reached the end of the line. The group under discussion were scarcely aware of the churchyard, and the idea that they might become vagrants never crossed their minds. They identified themselves with conventional society when it came to sleeping indoors, shaving, and eating at table.

But they often found great difficulty in keeping up appearances, and the relatives who cared for them suffered as much, or more, from the struggle to make ends meet. Many of the patients could not wash, and were physically as well as mentally ill.

In Mrs. Fehranbach's home there were patches of a different colour on walls and furniture, marking the places from which she had removed articles to sell or pawn. In the bay window eight narrow strips of curtain covered the window, each of a different pattern and texture to the next. A pile of clothes on a chair had been made ready to take to the wardrobe dealer. Her husband's jacket hung on the back of the chair where it seemed to have hung for a very long while; perhaps ever since he went to hospital two years before. The chairs and carpets were marked and stained, where she had patiently cared for an incontinent and confused man for eleven years before he was taken to hospital.

Miss Doreen Laven lived with her sister Hilda. Doreen Laven had not worked for more than twenty years: she was physically as well as mentally ill. Hilda had never earned more than £7 a week. Doreen had National Assistance out of which she kept 7s. 6d. pocket money. When the rent had been paid, the sisters had £3 10s. each to cover rates, light, heat, food, household goods, clothes, personal necessities and special items for the patient. These special items include extra warm clothing, adaptations to the furniture, special food, extra cleaning materials and 'little presents to cheer her up'. Miss Hilda Laven could not afford new clothes, and found hairdressing bills and savings for one week's holiday away every two years a great problem. Her social life became more narrow as the patient became more helpless. Her own bedroom was furnished with the old things, 'I keep meaning to refurnish it, but it never seems to get done,' she said lamely, and added that her appearance worried her. 'Stout people like me need to spend more on their clothes to look nice, don't they?' When the rents are increased she will have no rise in pay and does not know how she will manage.

Even when a husband is still working, the expenses of illness may run the household into difficulties. As one wife who had been in hospital explained, 'We had a lot of trouble before I got ill and we were scraping along helping my daughter out. There was me doing two part-time jobs as well as run the house and care for the grandchildren. Well, it was all too much for me and I had this breakdown. While I was ill we ran up a bill of £163. That's two years ago and we're still paying it off now.'

Although only one patient amongst the 86 could be considered rich, there were 38 living in households without financial worries. Even if they could not afford many luxuries, at least they could buy necessities without counting the pennies. Some, like Mrs. Chidley and her husband, were comfortably off. On the wall of their living-room were three small prints and in another room an oil painting, for which they had paid £27. The furniture was new and very expensive and in a corner stood a white maple cocktail cabinet. The hearth had a white fur rug in front of it. Mrs. Chidley, the patient, was very smartly dressed and had recently had her hair permanently waved. When she was ill for the first time her husband took her to Harley Street and to another specialist elsewhere, but when her mental troubles settled into a regular pattern he could no longer afford to let her be a private patient.

Saving for a holiday, which Miss Laven could only manage with great difficulty, once in two years, was no problem to Miss Dove or Mrs. Darnley, who both take holidays for granted as part of the natural pattern of events in the year. Mr. and Mrs. Darnley had a car and when at home they watched television or listened to records on their new record-player. Miss Dove, having refurnished her flat, decided to buy a tape-recorder.

Miss Dove, in spite of serious illness and hallucinations which have persisted for many years, has managed to remain in one job almost all her life, and is entirely self-supporting. Altogether 17 of the patients supported themselves out of their earnings, and seven of these were also responsible for wife, children or other relatives. Nineteen others depended mainly on a pension and 17 on National Assistance. The remainder were living on sickness or unemployment benefit. Sometimes families helped patients who also received Government aid. Table VII shows how the patients were supported at the time of entering hospital.

TABLE VII

PATIENTS' MEANS OF FINANCIAL SUPPORT AT TIME OF HOSPITAL ADMISSION

	Number	%
Employed and self-supporting.. ..	17	20%
Married women not in receipt of government aid	11	13%
Supported wholly by Government aid		
N.A.B. 7		
Unemployment or sickness benefit .. 10		
O.A.P. 8		
Sub-total	25	29%
Supported partly by Government aid, partly by family		
N.A.B. 9		
Unemployed or sickness benefit .. 12		
O.A.P. 11		
Sub-total	32	37%
Supported wholly by family	1	1%
Grand total	86	100%

Of the total of 72 patients, other than married women, 42% (30% of men and 59% of women) received at least some help from their families. For the majority the help was substantial. The single men, most of them, as we saw above, relatively young and with their parents still alive, are more likely to receive help than the married men.

Leaving aside the married women supported by their husbands and the 17 old-age pensioners, there were 55 who would normally have earned their living. In fact only 17 did so. Two-thirds received State help and nearly half of these were entirely dependent on it.

Thus one of the immediate effects of mental illness is that it jeopardizes the patient's economic security and often disturbs the finances of his family. It is usually this dilemma which brings the mentally sick person into contact with a network of services in the community. Though the primary problems of the sickness itself may long be kept hidden by the individual or his family, the means for alleviating the secondary problems come from the community. The next chapter moves on to consider the circumstances of the mentally sick and the provision made by society.

PART TWO
Community Services

VIII

THE PATIENT AND THE COMMUNITY

A healthy man controls diverse aspects of his life and accepts certain contacts with authority as necessary for himself and his family. But in sickness his life is parcelled out among many specialists for their direction and management; the sickness itself invites the attention of several different services,[1] while at the same time his personal affairs are delegated not to one, but to many. This process of fragmentation does not end with the patient; it extends to his family also.

By the nature of their illness mental patients are at a disadvantage in adapting themselves even to the normal range of contacts with the Employment Exchange, the Ministry of National Insurance, and similar bodies. Yet the more severe or chronic their illness the more they and their families come into contact with official and voluntary bodies.

This chapter, and the two which follow, describe the principal organizations concerned with patients in this area and discuss what help they are able to give in circumstances where mutual understanding is not easy. Whether they are national, county, borough or voluntary bodies, it will be more convenient here to classify the organizations and services by the aspect of the patients' lives with which they deal: employment, finance, health, housing, legal and advisory services, old-age services, religious organizations, and welfare.

---

[1] Throughout this chapter 'service' is used to include national and local administration as well as voluntary services.

99

The Employment Exchange

The Ministry of Labour Employment Exchange which serves this area is situated outside the borough. For most patients this meant either a journey on two buses or a walk of approximately two miles. Until recently mental patients applying for work had no special help unless it was directly requested. At the time these patients were in Long Grove Hospital, even if going to work outside the hospital each day, they were debarred from registration as disabled persons under the regulations in force.[1] They could apply for registration on their return home, but in practice few patients in the sample were aware of this right, to which they were entitled under the 1945 Disabled Persons Registration Regulations.

In the years covered by the survey—1956–57—liaison between Ministry of Labour, hospital and social welfare workers was steadily improving, but had not reached the standard brought about by the Mental Health Act of 1959 and the national interest aroused by the preceding Royal Commission. Only ten people out of 53 requiring employment on return from hospital were seen by the Disablement Resettlement Officer.[2] None of them were women. Four were placed in employment.

Theoretically, patients could apply or be nominated for training courses at a Ministry of Labour Rehabilitation Centre while still living in hospital, or after their return to the community. Only one of the patients in the sample did so, and was refused. In the years immediately following this survey, however, patients began to be accepted in the Rehabilitation Centres in limited numbers. But when they needed employment they could not apply for a place in a Remploy factory until after August 1959, and only two ex-patients have been known to do so since.

Some patients were referred to the Exchange by letter

[1] This ruling was altered in 1959.
[2] This area is served by a man and woman D.R.O. and their deputies.

from the hospital. In these cases the Exchange then invited the patient to attend for an interview. If this invitation was not accepted no follow-up was made and the papers were filed amongst the 'dormant' cases.

Ideally, patients should visit the Employment Exchange during leave periods some time before discharge, so that they are assured of work on their return. None of the ten sample patients seen by the D.R.O. achieved this ideal. Some patients were only home on week-end leave and little or nothing could be done for them on Saturday mornings. When the hospital did not notify the Ministry of Labour, the D.R.O. was not seen until long after the man had been 'signing on' at the Exchange, when he was referred for special help by an interviewing clerk.

Many of the 53 ex-patients seeking employment found their own work and very seldom were the Disablement Resettlement Officers, or any officials at the Exchange, notified of the patients' return and need of help. Since 1959, with increased co-operation, this situation has improved. But a number of patients still arrive at the Exchange saying, 'The doctor at the hospital told me to call', and there is delay while a medical report is obtained.[1]

Ex-patients who called at the Exchange as ordinary applicants for work were, of course, dealt with in the ordinary way. Some patients hid their mental illness and hospital experience from the Exchange staff. One such man was described by the D.R.O. (unaware of the man's illness) as having 'given up hope'—this was not considered a legitimate reason for not working. It is all too easy for such patients to become labelled as 'work-shy'; this patient was so classified by another less sympathetic officer elsewhere. If the patients did not explain their difficulties at the outset they were unlikely to make contact with the D.R.O. until their persistent failure to get or hold a job had attracted

---

[1] Under the regulations prevailing in 1956 and 1957 the D.R.O.s were unable to apply to the hospital for detailed reports. Without any information either in a referral letter or a report they were often handicapped in their work. The procedure regarding reports is now being altered.

special notice.[1] By this time loss of confidence, painful experience in unsuitable employment, and periods of unemployment and financial difficulty, had often made their problems much worse.

Because their work record was likely to be erratic or broken by long periods of sickness they soon exhausted their rights to unemployment benefit and found themselves under the joint jurisdiction of the National Assistance Board and the Ministry of Labour.

The judgement as to whether the applicant is fit for work rests with the doctor who advises the Exchange. This is the doctor appointed by the Regional Health Board. Psychiatric reports are only requested if thought necessary by the doctor, who meets the patient, often quite briefly and for the first time in his life, to decide 'Is this man fit for work?' Only the grossest mental abnormalities would be likely to show up under such circumstances. One schizophrenic man returned from such an examination with a form which stated that he was physically fit for work, and since he still did not sign on at the Exchange his assistance was disallowed. He then spent several months living partly on his relatives' generosity and partly on his earnings from casual employment, picking up a day here and a day there, when he could find it.

If an ex-patient fails to obtain or hold down a job over a number of years then he is likely to be considered for classification as unemployable. This decision depends upon a report from the D.R.O. and a careful consideration of the facts by the Advisory Committee of the Exchange, which includes a doctor among its members, but not a psychiatrist. This doctor is usually a general practitioner.[2]

Whether he reveals his stay in hospital and mental

[1] Although a member of the D.R.O.'s department in Epsom has been visiting the hospital regularly since 1947 (as a result of suggestions put forward in the 1945 Disabled Persons Registration Act), none of the 86 sample patients were seen in this way. For further details of this system see Appendix 3.

[2] See Forsyth, G., and Logan, R. F. L., *The Demand for Medical Care*, pp. 85–86, and p. 107.

problems or not, and whether he is dealt with at the Exchange by an interviewing clerk or by the D.R.O., the ex-mental patient's experience when he applies for work depends largely upon the definition of mental illness used by the person dealing with him. This varies not only according to temperament, training and experience, but also according to the pressure of work upon the official. He may be aware that the applicant before him has been in a mental hospital. Even so, the allowances he makes for this in what he expects from the applicant, and the way in which he decides that a job is suitable or unsuitable, are based on his own idea of what constitutes mental disturbance.

When asked what they regarded as 'mad behaviour', most workers in public organizations contacted during the present study first referred to paranoic symptoms and then to violence or to delusions of all kinds.[1] Depressives and withdrawn, quiet schizophrenics were rarely recognized as being mentally ill, though the depressives generally received sympathetic treatment. Withdrawn and apathetic ex-patients were usually labelled 'inadequate' when they were viewed kindly and 'work-shy' and 'lazy' when met with disapproval and exasperation. Psychopaths were almost universally thought of as 'crooks', 'twisters' and 'wide boys'. If they had made up their minds not to work, the view seemed to be, then it was a waste of time and energy to try to make them; after a 'testing' period, the Exchange staff appeared to ignore them as far as possible.

One officer exclaimed, 'Schizophrenic—what does that mean? I thought it was split personality, like Jekyll and Hyde, but I've got two people coming here, the doctor says they are schizophrenic—they are not a bit like that, and each is quite different from the other.' He is at a loss to know what type of employment to offer such ex-patients, and even if he knew what was suitable, he is restricted not only to the jobs that are available, but also to particular jobs with particular employers. The matching of skills to work,

---

[1] This question was asked at each organization visited.

temperament to temperament, and disabilities to work situation is a complicated and delicate matter. The decision as to what is suitable is inevitably subordinated to the officer's understanding of mental illness and to what is available.

It is difficult to influence the type of employer and employment available. But it should be possible to provide more information to Exchange staff, firstly about particular ex-patients (providing their permission has been gained), and secondly, about the effect on the mentally sick of noise, isolation, overcrowding, heat, light, swiftly moving machinery, night work, responsibility, and people. Staff at the Exchange did their best with the erratic and inadequate information they received from doctors, hospitals, and social workers. They had few opportunities to learn about mental illness, or the aspects of a job which matter most in resettlement. Though the Ministry of Labour has now had considerable experience of the mentally ill at both Waddon and Kidbrooke Training Centres, the lessons learned there have not always been passed on to D.R.O.s in areas where there are many mental patients.

The patients frequently complained, 'the man up the Labour doesn't understand my case—he sends me to jobs which are impossible'. They also complained of unhelpful advice, 'the doctor said I must have light work—the man at the Exchange said there is no light work in this area'. They felt that this was an official excuse and that 'light work' was kept for people who were not mental patients. They generally felt also that they were not given a fair chance by employers even when they could do the job, because either the employers or their workmates were frightened or prejudiced. However, some of the patients were not exactly easy to please. 'I want to work in the open with my hands at something interesting, but I can't start early because I feel pretty bad till about the middle of the morning and I'm frightened to be alone at night, so I can't work late either.' The man who said this did realize that he was asking a great deal, but he felt that it was his misfortune and not his fault and that 'the man up the Labour' ought to be able to find something which would meet his requirements.

At the time of the survey, out of 57 people who were not employed, only five attempted to avoid working, while seven had a breakdown precipitated or aggravated by being prevented from working (forcible retirement, redundancy, etc.) and one man had a 100 letters showing the desperate attempts he had made to get work after leaving hospital.

One of the difficulties centres around the meaning of 'reasonable employment'. The patients are sometimes unable, but more often unwilling, to explain why a particular job is 'unreasonable' or impossible for them. One middle-aged man could not bring himself to explain that he was so terrified of the dark that he insisted on sharing his bedroom with his aunt, and that he could not possibly work where it meant coming home alone in the dark in winter. He tries to overcome his fear, but is reduced to a state of physical collapse if left alone at night. In such an instance—and there were many others—the ex-patient's fears of ridicule, contempt or harshness make it difficult for him to explain the real reason for refusing or not holding the jobs offered to him. He may then easily be labelled as work-shy or unemployable, which is likely to be financially disastrous.

Since so many patients were economically dependent on their relatives, they could seldom feel much sense of worth and importance, and few were able to compensate for this by having any kind of status at work. Only a fifth of the patients of this study were working at all at the time when they were admitted to hospital: for the borough as a whole, the proportion would be 71% of people of similar ages. Moreover, the younger patients who feel most keenly their lack of dignity and significance in society make up the bulk of the unemployed patients. The average age of the unemployed patients was 36, of those at work, 45.

Eight of the patients had never worked and 17 had held a

skilled job for some time but, due to their illness, slithered into casual and unskilled employment. In six instances the patients had been either clerks or had owned their own business, and had then become casual labourers or unskilled workers.

In describing their difficulties over employment, the patients particularly mentioned that they could not tolerate such things as extremely competitive or fast-moving work, noise or confined spaces with lack of air. They were, above all, sensitive to personal relationships with their employers and workmates.

> 'It's the speed, it's as if they've got their foot behind you all the time; it's all that rushing all the time, and grab, grab, grab. I can't stand it. You have to keep up with the people on the machines or you hold them up. One day when the boss brought me another pile of work I tried to strangle him.'

> 'I can't bear to be indoors any more, I must get out where I can breathe, so I've applied for training as a gardener.'

> 'It's not that we're lazy, if you gave us a factory of our own with all of us together, we'd get more work done than anyone. It's the way the others look at you—"Oh don't talk to him, you want to watch him, he's been in the nut-house". And another thing, we like to be friendly and considerate to a person, we don't want anyone yelling their mouth off or pushing us about. I can't work if I get upset. What we'd do if we had a place of our own to work is to all help each other and have a nice sort of atmosphere.'

To avoid some of these problems, three of the patients had taken night work on their own, and others had taken jobs as sweepers or labourers, far below their intelligence, in order to avoid anxiety or particular forms of responsibility. But if the mentally ill often fail to achieve by their jobs the respect they would like to enjoy in the community, they are worse off if they do not work at all. Poverty apart, there is no place for them in the household during the working day. A sick husband or son only gets in the way of the housekeeping, and they are likely to find themselves pushed into a corner where they will be least nuisance, to brood on their problems.[1]

The National Assistance Board

The National Assistance Board office for this neighbourhood is right outside the area at the far end of an adjacent borough. But officers of the Board visit the applicant at home, if requested. Applicants can send a form, obtainable at a post office, with only their name and address on it. This has some disadvantages for ex-patients; they may be over-sensitive about asking for such a form or worried that they may not be able to fill it up, but most of all it deprives them of the opportunity to relieve their feelings by 'going up to the office to see them about it', when they feel worried or angry. But the number of applicants at this particular office is very heavy indeed and the officers cannot carry out visiting and assessment properly if they are constantly besieged by queues of applicants in the waiting room. For those who must call at the office, there are facilities for private interviews.

As was pointed out in the discussion of employment, mental patients are likely to become the joint concern of the National Assistance Board and the Ministry of Labour. Provided that he makes the usual declaration of financial circumstances and that these are within the limits allowed, a man who has been classified as 'unemployable' will be 'given a book' by the Assistance Board. He can then draw his money weekly near his home. But declarations of this sort are precisely those which paranoic patients are likely to refuse. Technical problems connected with payments to an agent acting for the patient, and the acceptability of statements from such a person then arise.

The Assistance Board recognizes the needs of the

---

[1] Men often meet the same problem after retirement if they have no hobbies or voluntary work to occupy their time. See Townsend, P., *The Family Life of Old People*, p. 147.

unemployable. But the 'work-shy' will not be accepted. A patient who was unofficially classified as 'work-shy' was given three weeks warning by the Assistance Board and on the fourth week he was refused assistance on the grounds that he had refused 'reasonable employment'. It can therefore make a great difference to a mentally disturbed man whether he is considered unemployable or merely unreasonable about the work he will accept. But when, for example, is a young, able-bodied, but withdrawn, schizophrenic able to work and when not?

The National Assistance Board rely upon the medical report from the Ministry of Labour, but the doctor making this report, as I have said, is rarely a psychiatrist and never a doctor who has known the man over a period of time. As with employment, the experience of the mentally disturbed person seeking assistance depends largely upon the officer's personal definition of mental illness. National Assistance Board staff are even less likely than D.R.O.s to have received any training about mental illness. The one course in the London area was voluntary and not a part of regular training, though it was well attended.

National Assistance Board officers pointed out, with obvious justification, that they cannot be all things to all men. More than half the cases dealt with by this area office concern supplementary assistance to old-age pensioners, or full assistance for the elderly. The remainder are the physically handicapped, deserted wives, the mentally defective and the mentally disordered. The latter are less than 1% of the people dealt with in the area. The staff officers with whom the problem was informally discussed felt that a disproportionate amount of time would be needed to study the mentally sick.

But the proportion of mentally disturbed people at home in the community is likely to increase with the new emphasis on community care. Even now the percentage quoted above is an underestimate, since amongst those in receipt of assistance there are ex-mental patients not recognized as mentally ill, and over and above those are the patients who would not apply for assistance a second time after they have once been refused, and who 'get by' with casual work, help from relatives and sometimes by begging. (Two of the patients in the sample were known to beg when in difficulties and a third followed an intricate system of borrowing.)

Providing the mental sickness of the applicants was already clearly established when the officers first dealt with them, sympathetic co-operation was immediately forthcoming. The patience and help extended to certain families where several members were known to be mentally ill was remarkable. The calculations of the distribution of rent allowances alone in such a family calls for tact and ingenuity since any system evolved for the sake of perfect justice must be easily modifiable, when several members of the household may be intermittently in hospital. The restraint, goodwill and fairness shown by the officers dealing with such families was remarkable. But this was where the patient or the family was obviously very disturbed, or where the ex-patient had been referred by another agency.

The Assistance Board officers, in their own minds, ask themselves about each application: Does the applicant's situation fit the regulations or does some element debar him? Is the situation his fault or not? If it is, should I help him or not? Shall I help him obtain the maximum or the minimum service? Is he capable of helping himself? Shall I let him be dependent or try to force him to be independent?

'Is he entitled to Assistance?' would appear to require a plain 'yes' or 'no'. In practice there are many borderline cases where the discretion of the officer is the deciding factor and then his value judgements, emotions and experience are all brought into play. Certain types of mentally ill people present a 'negative' image to the Assistance officer; they may be proud, secretive, shy and unwilling, or unable, to communicate with others. They may appear to dodge work because they cannot or will not explain why it is intolerable. They may look physically fit and sound perfectly sensible when interviewed. If they are not at first greeted with sympathy or understanding they may become over-sensitive, frightened or angry and may not apply for Assistance again. Their illness may affect them only in certain ways or in certain situations which are not immediately obvious. One man, labouring under a compulsion, had to visit a particular street on the other side of London and knock at a door before he could sleep. His bus fares reduced the money he had available for food: should the Assistance Board recognize or ignore his special problem? By visiting this street each night he kept himself out of hospital. As a hospital patient he cost the government more than twice as much as he received from the Assistance Board.

It was noticeable that senile people received considerable care and attention—far more than the 'relief of immediate need'. When mental illness was combined with old age it never went unrecognized. Whatever the pressure of work and the nature of the training, Assistance Board officials, like all the members of the organizations interviewed, were very ready to make allowances for the old and the infirm, and therefore quick to notice and to answer their need for help and kindness. The young able-bodied patient always met with most resistance, suspicion or even open hostility, unless the fact of his mental illness was very firmly understood by the officer dealing with him. If the Assistance Board staff knew from sources other than the applicant himself that he was or had been a patient they were usually most helpful.

Without further research it is impossible to say how many ex-patients who are 'refused' or not recognized by the Assistance Board turn to begging, casual employment, or deteriorate into tramps. Only three patients in this sample were found in such circumstances, but several more were noticed among their friends. Recognition could be made easier if the hospitals provided the National Assistance

Board with more information and if their officials were trained to deal with the mentally sick, particularly the withdrawn patients.

Further problems arose over the appointment of agents to receive the money. Some patients returning home flatly refused to apply for Assistance because they thought it was shameful. Their relatives could only keep them at home if they obtained it. A patient returning to one area was accepted as a person of sound mind—being 'cured'—and therefore his refusal to apply was upheld as his right; and in the other area, near by, his mother was made the agent and the patient's refusal was overruled.

Other difficulties arose from confusion and ignorance. Welfare workers and doctors often had little or no idea about some of the regulations, while some of the patients mistakenly but adamantly refused to apply 'because it will be no use'. For example, one elderly father prevented his mentally disturbed son from finishing a temporary job which had been given him because he believed that it would result in them both losing their Assistance grant for the week. It was only after considerable argument and an assurance from the National Assistance Board that he accepted the fact that Leslie could receive 30s. for his work without reducing his Assistance. Similarly none of the six G.P.s asked[1] knew that patients receiving National Assistance could reclaim prescription charges at the nearest post-office on presenting a chit from the chemist or dispenser. The patients themselves were also unaware of this although the information is printed in their Assistance books. Other families firmly believed that the receipt of any kind of welfare grant, pension or earnings debarred them from applying for Assistance. Very few were aware that under certain circumstances they could become agents for their mentally sick relatives.

---

[1] Six G.P.s out of 26 covering different areas of the borough were asked questions about National Assistance to check the general impression that such regulations were not known.

Ministry of Pensions and National Insurance

Insurance cards were a worry to those whose employment was erratic. Many claimed 'small income exception' so that they need not stamp their cards, and then when they took a job for a few weeks became confused as to what they should do about stamps. Most of the patients with such problems found their way, not to the Insurance office, but to the local Citizens' Advice Bureau or one of the Settlements where they could find someone to complete the necessary forms for them.

Patients wishing to start working again after a very long stay in hospital had another difficulty. They had to explain their blank card to a prospective employer. If they said nothing, the employer might think they had been in prison, and if they said 'I've been in hospital', the employer would naturally inquire about the reason. Several patients complained that if they said 'mental hospital' it was 'enough to ensure losing the job'. Mr. Colt having failed to obtain several jobs in this way, actually injured his knee, so that he could claim that he had been in hospital with a complicated leg injury. He then applied for the job of clerk/warehouseman and was refused on the grounds that 'it wouldn't be right to give you this job if you've been in hospital with your leg *that* long, because you have to shift heavy boxes'.

Housing

Since so many of the patients were not working, or held irregular and poorly paid jobs, they were poorer than most of their neighbours. As a result they more often lived in the worst houses of the borough. Even if they were not poor, fewer of them were locally-born, and so less likely to have the relatives and friends who would tell them about tenancies. Small but complete houses[1] with their own back

---

[1] Since this study was made, more and more of these terraced cottages have been demolished, and in the future, most of the people in the area will be tenants of Council flats.

yards are very much sought after, and tenancies which become vacant are 'spoken for' by mothers whose daughters are getting married, or by relatives long established locally who wish to have their kin near by. A long standing friendship with the rent collector and a good rent record help to obtain such tenancies.

The blocks of old 'Dwellings', many of them built in the 1890's or earlier, are least popular as homes. Access to flats in them is therefore easier for the stranger. The dwellings have many disadvantages. Tenants must often fetch water from a communal tap and share a common lavatory with other tenants. Quarrelling over the wash-house or at the tap made things worse for elderly and paranoic patients.

As a group the mental patients are badly housed compared with their neighbours. More of them shared flats in old dwellings or in split-up 3-storey houses, and fewer were in terraced cottages than in a matched sample from the population in the borough at large, as is shown in Table VIII.

TABLE VIII

HOUSING, PATIENTS COMPARED WITH A SAMPLE OF THE POPULATION OF THE SURVEY BOROUGH

	Patients	Survey Borough Sample
Cottages		
2-storey type	24%	35%
3-storey type (shared)	21%	12%
Flats		
Council flats	32%	26%
'Dwellings' *	23%	21%
Other**	—	6%
Total %	100%	100%
Number	86	500

* Multi-storey blocks of flats usually built before 1914 by Charitable Associations.
** Flats over shops, attached to business premises, etc.

The relationship between private landlords and mentally disturbed tenants was not explored. The information which follows is about Council housing only. Council 'landlords' are welfare workers and landlords at the same time. At times both housing managers and housing welfare officers found that this dual responsibility led to conflicting feelings, particularly in dealing with mentally ill tenants. It was not always possible to be both a good landlord and a good friend.

No mentally sick person has been rehoused from the borough waiting list in the last five years (i.e. since 1955) and only two people from the survey sample have been rehoused as a result of slum clearance. Both were single patients living alone, one an elderly woman and the other a middle-aged man. Such people are a very considerable problem to the housing authorities. The single-person accommodation in the borough is extremely limited. Weary of waiting to be rehoused, a number of these lone persons on the borough slum-clearance rehousing list go off to find their own rooms or accommodation elsewhere. Both in the borough and county rehousing schemes provision is made for single elderly people. But the area which includes the survey borough has such a high proportion of elderly people that they have very little chance. The young unmarried male schizophrenic or the middle-aged depressive unmarried man or woman have very little hope compared with married people of the same age. If young single people are living in *furnished* accommodation in slum clearance property it has been the custom of the County Council to ask them to rehouse themselves. Those with their own furniture took their turn with the married applicants. It has been County Council policy to give some of the mentally ill certain priorities on medical grounds. But in relation to their total number in East London alone, very, very few have yet been rehoused.

But some mental patients are, of course, living in Council property. Three incidents will serve to illustrate some of the problems they cause.

Mr. Hope is normally an excellent tenant, quiet, hard-working, keeping himself to himself and living an ordinary life. When he becomes ill, however, he loses his sense of place and time and wanders off, unmindful of the state of his home. In one fortnight he chopped firewood in his living-room at 2 a.m., damaging the room and annoying the neighbours; left a stew on the gas and wandered away from home for two days far from the fumes and small fire he left behind him; left his laundry boiling and caused another fire; did his housework in the middle of the night; left the electric lights and gas on and finally threatened a neighbour with an axe. The caretaker could rarely get hold of Mr. Hope, since he usually returned and departed in the middle of the night. Mr. Hope eventually walked into the mental hospital himself while the authorities and his employer were searching for him.

Mr. Plant left the tap running in the sink and the gas on and went away from home. After three days the flat beneath became flooded and neighbours along the corridor complained of gas. When the flat door was broken down letters from welfare officers and the hospital, informing Mr. Plant of the date for his voluntary admission to hospital, were found floating in several inches of water. Three flats required repairs and Mr. Plant's relatives suffered considerable loss to the carpets and possessions which were ruined in their absence.

Miss Pravdin, a senile patient living alone, absent-mindedly left the tap running and flooded her neighbour's flat five times in one year. Finally the D.A.O. was called by the housing welfare officer and she was admitted to hospital.

Such patients were a danger to themselves, by reason of their absent-mindedness, just as much as those who threatened or attempted suicide. A large proportion of housing welfare officers' time is spent in visiting, talking to and cajoling such people and their immediate neighbours.

While seven of the survey patients caused trouble to their neighbours it is equally true that neighbours or housing problems can cause suffering to the patients. This was so in five[1] families. Mrs. Mayerat was frightened to go down and

---

[1] These facts were confirmed by reference to people outside the patient's family and by personal observation.

answer the door because of the verbal and physical attacks by her neighbour. She also suffered from having coal stolen and her flat entered by the neighbour's children.

Because they may be out of work and unable to pay the rent regularly, mentally sick people sometimes find themselves in the older flats with the impecunious and even the criminal.

> Isobel Griffiths' family became an easy prey to a group of hooligans in their block of flats. Isobel herself was frightened to go into the communal yard because her brothers had been injured in fights with the neighbours' children. While her family were not without their own rather doubtful habits, Isobel was nervous, sensitive, withdrawn and silently well-behaved. She was quite unable to stand up to the pressure of living in close contact with violence and had a serious breakdown at the age of fifteen.

> Mrs. Valdar and Miss Plastow, new to the neighbourhood, were treated with suspicion as foreigners. Miss Paul was also unfortunate in living next to a woman who could not tolerate her eccentric behaviour at the communal tap and her paranoic fears of interference. Miss Paul undoubtedly behaved in a strange way and also quarrelled easily, but might well have carried on quietly in her own room, as she did before this neighbour's arrival, if the woman had not constantly frightened and threatened her with being put away.

The housing officers felt that such people required intensive case-work help, especially during bad phases, or immediately on their return from hospital. This was when the trouble started. Neighbours were normally very tolerant, according to the welfare officers, but fire, flooding, and gas, banging and noise during the night, or bad language and paranoic accusations during the day are naturally liable to strain the neighbours' tolerance.

In one officer's words, 'The Council bend over backwards to prevent the eviction of these people, but we have to think of the neighbours and relatives sometimes too. There is a tremendous conflict of loyalties in the family of mentally sick people. But even when we have obtained their co-operation, the situation tends to break down eventually. We need special help to deal with such problems. The psychiatrists are completely remote from our difficulties. Dealing with people in hospital is totally different. We want to know how to help such people at home. The "pre-fabs" are sometimes the answer—but they have a limited "life" and even then there are problems. For example, one tenant threw plates through the windows of the next house and another scattered dangerous drugs in the garden where the neighbours' children could pick them up.'

Another officer felt that there should be an equivalent of the probation service for the mentally sick, so that a particular person was responsible for the welfare of each mental patient in the community. The advantages of the old Relieving Officer were again mentioned. The co-ordinating committee set up to provide links between all health and welfare organizations within each medical division of the L.C.C. might help in these difficulties. The purpose of the committee is to prevent precisely the over-visiting and conflicting advice complained of by some patients. At present this committee appears to be wholly occupied in discussing families where there are young children and rent arrears. This excludes a large number of the mentally sick who are unmarried and often living alone.

In the desire to minimize disturbance, some patients have been housed in corner flats on the ground floor so that they have no neighbours on one side or underneath them, no balconies and no communal rubbish chutes. An interview conducted in one such flat showed the price paid. Children roller-skating at speed down a cement strip used the flat wall as a buffer. Others played ball against the end of the same wall. Several cracked and broken windows bore witness to this. On the inner wall the foot of the communal staircase was a few feet from the front door and the exit passage ran along another wall. When dustbins were emptied near the window and when a boy sat on the cement ledge outside to play a trumpet, it was impossible to carry on a conversation in the flat. Senile patients and unemployed or physically sick mental patients who cannot go out suffer considerably in such places. But if they are placed in a flat in the middle of a third floor landing, they may, when they are noisy themselves, disturb half a dozen families. Further co-operation between architects, administrators, doctors and housing and welfare officers is needed to work out better solutions than have been found so far.

IX

HEALTH SERVICES

THE mental patient living in this area may come into contact with a very wide range of health services. There are at least 23 different types of medical help available; one patient had been to as many as eight different medical 'agencies'. This was exceptional—the majority saw only their own G.P., the Long Grove psychiatrist and the Long Grove social worker.

The general practitioner

At the time of the survey there were 26 general practitioners serving 53,000 people in the borough. Twenty-nine of the patients and their relatives described their doctor as a well-known family friend to whom they were devoted. They were especially grateful when the doctor had restored order to a household which had lost it. Hilda Maxted's family explained how their G.P. had helped them survive a day of violence while they waited for the D.A.O. He spent an hour with the patient in the morning and returned three or four times in the day. He also sent his junior partner to stay until Hilda was safely ushered into the ambulance some nine hours later. Miss Richardson relied on her doctor to comfort her when her delusions overwhelmed and terrified her. She always flew to the surgery for protection, and was never refused it.

Thirty spoke of their doctor in a matter-of-fact way as somebody necessary, seen as rarely as possible, having no strong relationship with the family. Fifteen referred to the G.P. with open hostility and blamed him for not recognizing, or for mistreating, the patient's illness. They were most bitter when the doctor had failed to help them in a particular crisis. Mr. and Mrs. Freedman described how they had to fetch the police after the doctor had refused to attend to their son during the night when he began to smash the furniture. Mr. Griffiths was even more bitter about the G.P. who attended his daughter when she ate less and less over a period of eight months till she was too weak to wash herself or drink unaided. Mrs. Davies changed her doctor after the only advice he offered about her husband's manic-depression was to get a divorce. Ten of the other 12 families never saw their G.P. The two remaining patients, both young men schizophrenics, had wandered about the London area and had no doctor. In the experience of a N.A.B. officer, such young men rarely have a doctor.

As was shown in Chapter II, the G.P. rarely initiated an admission. The doctor who attended Miss Richardson and Mr. Churchley thought they were ill, but not that he should advise psychiatric treatment. 'Why should I?' he said, 'it won't cure them, and they are no trouble to anyone very much at home.' (This was not the view of Mr. Churchley's family, who felt his illness had broken up the home.) 'They just need helping along. They would be very miserable in a place like Long Grove, why not leave them alone?'

Mr. Jackson's doctor, while agreeing reluctantly to refer him to the out-patient clinic, definitely advised against the mental hospital—it was no place for pleasant, sensitive young men like Mr. Jackson, he said.

Even the doctors attending Mr. Swallow and Mrs. Fryers, who recognized the nature of their illness and arranged for mental hospital admission, felt that the name 'Epsom' and the identity of the 'hospital in the country' should be disguised from the patients at the time of admission. They did not recommend admission with any confidence. In Mr. Swallow's family this deception led to considerable resentment and quarrelling before peace was restored.

Mr. Wrigg's doctor felt that, once the patient had returned home, he needed long term psychotherapeutic support. At the expense of much time and energy this the doctor provided himself. Mr. Wrigg called when he felt like it and did not attend the out-patient clinic.

Miss Plastow's and Mr. Naughton's families felt that they understood the patients very much better than the doctor. They either ignored him or worked to cajole him into giving the pills or the treatment they had decided to have. Mrs. Newman sat at home for four months with puerperal depression until the Health Visitor arranged for her immediate admission to hospital.

The general impression confirms the findings of the Nuffield Report.[1] Psychiatric problems are sometimes not recognized at all by G.P.s; when they are, doctors are sometimes unaware of the services and treatment available; when these services are known, the doctors are not always in sympathy with the methods of treatment or the institutions available. On the other hand, little appears to be done in the psychiatric services to add to understanding. Some psychotic and neurotic patients continue to absorb the time, energy and patience of the doctor in the surgery when they have not been to the out-patients department or the mental hospital, others shun the doctor's help even for physical ailments when they have experienced psychiatric treatment.

The missions

The borough has two Medical Missions, and a Catholic hospice for the dying near by. Wherever medicine and religion combined, the patients and their families felt they had a special relationship with the clinic, whether they shared the religious faith or not. They expected a particularly personal service and had great trust in the doctors. They were not disappointed. There was no suggestion that

---

[1] Forsyth, G., and Logan, R. F. L., *The Demand for Medical Care*, pp. 85–86 and p. 107.

they were treated from the medical point of view in a different way from those who went to ordinary G.P.s. But the sympathy and interest which they found in the mission clinics seemed to make the secondary effects of mental disturbance easier to tolerate. When crisis threatened there was always someone to whom they could talk.

One medical mission has a staff of four doctors with whom residents in the area can register in the normal way. The mission has also mother and baby clinics and family planning clinics. In addition to the medical work, Bible reading and religious meetings are held during the week and Sunday school on Sundays.

Four of the survey patients were registered at this mission, and the staff knew of 20 mentally sick people with whom they dealt regularly. At the time of the interview they hoped to extend the psychiatric services of the mission as they felt this was needed, especially amongst certain problem families where they intended to start child guidance work.

Five of the patients had been out-patients or in-patients at another mission. This hospital has one 2-hourly psychiatric clinic a week, where the hospital almoner acts as psychiatric social worker. About a dozen patients (including two or three new patients) are seen each week. Most of them are adolescents and over-tired mothers with young families.

Only one patient from the sample entered the hospice. His relatives were delighted by the individual care and attention which he received, and were especially touched by the welcome given to all the family whenever they called. The children were made welcome and all of them invited to help raise funds for the wards. Mrs. Brown said, 'I couldn't bear to see him go to die away from home, but they've got the facilities to make him comfortable so much more than I have, and they are so good to him. They treat him like a relative and he's so happy there. When the children visit him they take things for Reverend Mother's fund and she blesses them. I'm not a Catholic myself, but the nuns are wonderful nurses. I can't say enough for them.'

While the patients and their relatives appreciated the friendly informal atmosphere which they found in the missions, this was mixed with the tendency to make decisions for the patients in an autocratic manner. Since the attitude was paternal the mission staff defended this behaviour by saying that it was all done for the patients good (even, for example, the 'kidnapping' of Miss Richardson). Similarly, because of the mission's previous voluntary status, and, even more, because of their religious values, decisions about patients were often made with little reference to other services (which did not share the beliefs and attitudes of the mission) but which were in contact with the same patient.

Borough health services

The borough medical officer and public health department were only mentioned in connexion with housing problems. Two senile patients who hoarded insanitary rubbish or became infested with vermin were dealt with by its staff.

One Health Visitor covers the main parts of the borough, but small sections of it are served by two others. They do not see much of mental patients. Most of their work is with mothers and babies, whereas a high proportion of mental patients are either unmarried or elderly. But more attention is apparently being paid to neuroses and generally disturbed behaviour among mothers. Although only one mother amongst the patients in the sample was referred directly by a Health Visitor for psychiatric treatment, between them they knew of a number of other mothers who were seriously disturbed. They said that they would welcome more information about community care and services for the mentally sick, and above all more help in how to recognize mental illness when they meet it. When they did recognize it they acted promptly to obtain treatment.

District nurses were only mentioned twice by the patients and their families, once in connexion with nursing a bedridden senile patient and once in connexion with a leg injury in an elderly patient.

Services for the mentally defective

Four of the patients in the survey suffered from mental defect as well as psychoses and thus came into contact with the local organizer for the supervision of mental defectives as well as the services for the mentally disordered. The experience of these few patients serves to illustrate the advantages and disadvantages of the differing types of service.

Unlike the erratic contacts of the psychotics with welfare authorities, marked by sudden crises and intense activity, alternating with periods of no contact at all, the defective psychotics' contacts with the authorities tended to begin early and progress steadily in a stable manner. Two patients, for instance, had been under the care of the same organizer for more than 20 years. The other two, having moved into the area in adult life, had more tenuous relationships; in fact one of them, a young man in his thirties, managed to evade supervision by his unsettled way of life. But if they had continuity of care and long-standing friendly relationships with the supervisors, the mentally defective patients (prior to the 1959 Act) had much less freedom than the mentally disordered. The latter could enter hospital voluntarily from 1930 onwards, while the former could only do so after the 1959 Act. Before this, the defectives entering an institution came entirely under the jurisdiction of the County Council and only returned to the total care and legal guardianship of their families after two years at home 'on licence'. Even after this they generally continued with voluntary supervision.

On returning from hospital after a period of psychotic illness, these four defective patients found themselves under the care of welfare officers from two sources, but in practice co-operation between the officers concerned usually prevented duplication of visiting. However, serious differences of opinion concerning the patient and his family did sometimes arise. Mr. Ransom wished to return home from hospital to which the hospital raised no objection, but the organizer for work with defectives considered that this was not in the interests of Mrs. Ransom and the children.

Under the 1959 Act the work with both defectives and the mentally disordered is being amalgamated at a local level. Mental welfare officers will work with both types of patients in future. After-care systems for both are being re-organized and new schemes being evolved. But for those patients who suffered the double misfortune of defect and psychosis at the time of this survey, the conflict between the regulations was extremely confusing. As voluntary patients they could choose to enter or discharge themselves from a mental hospital, but discharge normally resulted in them returning to legal guardianship or supervision outside hospital as defectives. They could not initiate their own entry to an institution as a defective. When they were visited at home one 'welfare lady' had to be obeyed, the other did not.

Community psychiatric social workers

Only four patients came into contact with the community psychiatric care service. The 1959 Mental Health Act gives priority to its development and in November 1960 this service of the L.C.C. was completely reorganized.[1]

When the National Health Service Act came into force in 1948, L.C.C. social workers in county mental hospitals were absorbed by the Ministry of Health and the L.C.C. was left without any such staff of its own. For the time being voluntary bodies, as the L.C.C. Medical Officer said in his 1957 Report, acted for the Council. 'In London the work was first carried on by the National Association for Mental Health and the Mental After-Care Association, jointly acting as agents of the Council, but from April 1953 the service was undertaken directly by the Council which,

---

[1] After this date the work of the community P.S.W.s was organized on a divisional basis and included work with defectives as well as the disordered.

since then, has been building its own service by the direct engagement of psychiatric social workers under the general direction of the consultant psychiatrist employed by the Council as its adviser in mental health. In 1955 the number of psychiatric social workers rose to four—one of the positions becoming a senior post during 1957. During 1957, when for seven months there were only three pyschiatric social workers in the department, approximately 500 referrals were accepted of which 269 (54%) were thought to call for at least one visit, and 231 (46%) were dealt with on an advisory basis.'[1]

The work of the community psychiatric care and after-care department is envisaged by its personnel, and by the medical and psychiatric officers supervising it, as falling into three main sections: namely, preventive-care, after-care and consultative help. Preventive-care is described in the 1957 Report as being help offered to the person who is over-anxious and under pressure which he feels to be intolerable, and which is indirectly expressed in psychosomatic illness without the sufferer understanding its causes. After-care, as the word implies, is the work undertaken by the community psychiatric social worker after the patient has returned home from mental hospital or concluded treatment elsewhere. Consultative help is the advice given to other agencies or workers already dealing with a mentally sick person. 'This type of interpretative work increased steadily through 1957 and it is hoped that it will continue to do so, as it has obvious advantages of continuity of relationship for the patient, economy of effort for the workers involved, and the two-way exchange of views on the situation.'[2]

Referrals to this department came from more than 46 sources, but the largest single source was the mental hospitals. Very few referrals were from general practitioners. As I have said, only four of the patients in the present study were seen by the community psychiatric social

---

[1] *Report* of the L.C.C. Medical Officer of Health 1957.
[2] Ibid.

workers in 1956 and 1957. Two were referred by relatives, one by a probation officer and one by a welfare worker. The work carried out by the L.C.C. psychiatric social workers in 1956 and 1957 was concentrated in the south and south-west of London rather than the east and north-east. The area in which the survey borough is situated had the lowest number of referrals and the least help.

There are a number of reasons for this. Firstly, the survey borough is awkwardly placed geographically, between the centres at which community P.S.W.s interviewed people, and few patients were willing to adopt the alternative and travel to County Hall.

Secondly, social workers, like other professional workers, are influenced by their particular interests and also by their different training. Thus one specialist working in a neighbourhood not only develops a local bias but also sees the situation differently from other specialists. This sometimes results in conflicts of attitude among the workers themselves; and these conflicts help to explain why the community psychiatric social workers played so small a part in the survey area at the time of the study.

A high proportion of patients admitted from the survey borough were either senile or chronic psychotics. To the local workers who meet such patients every day, John Smith may seem highly eligible for the attention of the community P.S.W. Since she deals with a wide range of all types of patient from a much larger and less specific area, however, she may regard him as quite unsuitable. If this situation arises frequently between a particular area and a particular P.S.W., misunderstanding is bound to arise, and since all the people engaged in this work tend to be overworked and under-staffed, poor communications and lack of awareness of the total nature of each other's work and difficulties are perpetuated.

The distance between the hospital and the catchment area added to this problem, and for the same reason fewer domiciliary visits by the hospital psychiatrists were carried out in this area than in other parts of London. Therefore less referrals to the community P.S.W.s were made directly by psychiatrists from this area.

When a new service, such as the community care and after-care, is offered, established organizations are apt to think that it is there only to share existing problems whereas it may be to fulfil some purpose not previously catered for at all. To some extent the community care department has undertaken the service of a population not otherwise dealt with, rather than taking some of the load from many existing organizations. The failure of some local workers to appreciate this again appears to have contributed to professional conflicts and antagonisms.

To sum up, the reasons for the inadequate contact between the survey area and the community psychiatric social workers in 1956 and 1957 seem to be as follows.

(1) Insufficient staff and several changes of staff.
(2) The distance of local offices from the borough, and of mental hospitals from East London.
(3) Failures in the system by which patients were referred.
(4) Lack of communication in general between general practitioners and the department.
(5) Lack of communication between the community psychiatric social workers and some workers with specialist training in other fields.
(6) Conflicting attitudes to problems of mental illness arising from different aims.
(7) Lack of knowledge about cultural differences within the communities in the area, and lack of information about the distribution of mental illness in general and the concentration of particular types of illness.

This short account of some of the people whose purpose is to serve the mental patient shows what a tangle it was. From the point of view of the patient what he saw was a large number of rather baffling organizations, with staff scattered about at varying distances from his home, offering fragmentary, intermittent care. And that was not the end of it.

X

OTHER WELFARE SERVICES

THERE are both a Legal Advice Bureau and Citizens'
Advice Bureau in the borough. Seven patients had
made use of the former, four the latter, while three were
well known to both. They sought advice on divorce, illegiti-
macy, guardianship, landlords, compensation for industrial
injury, property rights in family possessions, defence in a case
of assault, proceedings against neighbours for alleged theft,
tax problems and insurance, while some came with requests
for food, clothes, accommodation and even financial support.

The C.A.B. and Legal Advice Service show how welfare
organizations may fulfil therapeutic functions for which
they were not originally intended. The C.A.B. in the
borough remains in contact with a group of destitute and
semi-destitute mentally disturbed people who prefer their
own kind of freedom, in spite of poverty and lack of housing, to any institution. They refuse, or are unable, for complicated and eccentric reasons, to comply with the regulations which would entitle them to National Assistance.
They call at the C.A.B. at irregular intervals, partly to get
some practical help, mainly for the friendly and permissive
relationship which they are able to establish with the
people there, without fear of compulsion, ridicule or misunderstanding. Without this help some of them would
inevitably be in the senile or chronic wards of a mental
hospital. Other mental patients with a stronger hold on life
in the community also come regularly for sympathy.

A similar group of chronic psychotics and some very

neurotic people keep in touch with the Legal Advice Bureau and come frequently to relieve their feelings in lengthy talks. Sympathy and friendly suggestions, added to the legal advice which they receive, has helped many of them to retain a place in the community. Psychiatric treatment or care is sometimes suggested, but if they choose to ignore it no pressure is brought to bear upon them.

In both these organizations the staff has remained the same over a long time, so that new relationships do not constantly daunt the caller. The offices are also known and easily accessible and someone is always available. Continuity is therefore maintained.

Services for the elderly

Within the borough there are many good clubs and services for the elderly. There are over 8,000 elderly people in the borough; approximately 1,000 are housebound. There are two borough welfare officers and an organizer dealing with this work. There is a day centre with one full-time organizer and one Settlement, part-time help being given by the residents. This day centre provides meals, keep-fit classes, leisure activities, discussion groups and outings for the elderly, and also organizes a small but very popular workshop, which is expanding steadily. Other special clubs for the elderly are held in three other settlements and at the Congregational church. The majority of churches and other settlements have a special welcome for the elderly in some of their general activities. Contact is maintained with the people both elderly and mentally sick who have attended clubs and centres, even though they cannot attend any longer. Senile patients living at home are visited; 'meals on wheels' are supplied if necessary as well as 'home helps'. There is also chiropody and hairdressing. People are accompanied to and from their homes, if they wish, and someone stays with them if they are disturbed or upset. The G.P. is notified if they seem ill or not taking prescribed drugs. In general, as one elderly person put it, they are helped, to 'keep their feet under their own table', instead of drifting into hospital.

Isolated elderly people are notified to the Old People's Welfare Association by doctors, milkmen, electricity and gas-meter men, neighbours and the clergy. In spite of this, both the welfare visitors for the elderly and the City Missioner[1] (who visits every house in this area at regular intervals) still find some distressing neglect amongst the elderly and senile; the D.A.O.s also said that some senile people were admitted to hospital in a very bad condition. It is difficult to reconcile a humane and comprehensive service for the senile people living in the area with the requirements of freedom and non-interference. To what extent should senile patients be allowed to harm themselves because they wish to remain alone at home?

Twenty-one of the sample patients were over pensionable age (14 women and seven men). Despite what has been said above about the services for those capable of using them, only one man and three women were in contact with the old people's welfare service or attended any club. Six women were not in touch with any organization; four of these were neglected and in need of care when they were admitted to hospital. Only two of the elderly men lived alone, but one was in a neglected state when admitted to hospital. Though the services for the elderly sustained a number of the mentally ill, these were old people who had become mentally sick, rather than long-term mental patients who had become old. The elderly mentally sick were, on the whole, not those who sought help and companionship in clubs and group activities. The younger patients did not join organized group activities very often and had difficulty in mixing with such groups, and there is no reason to expect that they would become more sociable as they got older. Some elderly patients were, however, able to accept a friendly 'home help' as a substitute for relatives.

[1] The City Missioners are a group of Nonconformist evangelical missionaries who carry out regular house-to-house visiting, police-court work and work with children in the City of London.

Religious organizations

As a whole the patients were no more active church-goers than the majority of people in East London. Sixty-eight of them never went to church and only eight went regularly. So it is not surprising that few of them mentioned help from religious bodies. The Jewish Board of Guardians had sent visitors to four of the patients and the Methodist church two. Four patients, who were regular weekly attenders at church when at home, were neither visited nor received any help from their church.

The attitudes of the clergy varied considerably. One man explained that in a congregation of 60 adults, 12 were mentally ill and that both he and a church worker spent a considerable amount of time visiting and befriending the families concerned. A rota of visitors went from the church to the mental hospital at Epsom. Several of the clergy thought that the mentally ill should be dealt with by the medical profession. One man felt that he was already unable to cope with the numbers of normal parishioners who needed his services and that specialist training, which he did not possess, would be required before he could attempt to do much for the mentally ill. Another was very willing to visit or help, but felt that the sense of stigma in the borough was still very strong and that the mentally sick were 'kept hidden' when the vicar called. He also felt that there was a gulf between working people and the church in general and that this prevented the mentally sick and their relatives in East London from seeking help from the church. Another clergyman said that he had occasionally visited mental patients in the past, but was unaware of any in the parish at the moment.

There are no hostels or boarding houses run by religious bodies in the borough itself, but almost all of the Settlements have religious connexions and are residential. (The part played by the Settlements is discussed later.) One religious organization has no church in the neighbourhood, and no buildings, but sends it workers into all the homes in the area. This is the London City Mission which sends a City Missioner to visit every household in the section of the borough appointed to him. A local Missioner explained that many of the people whom he visited most regularly were isolated and mentally sick. In an area consisting of some 30 streets, which include many blocks of flats and tenements, he could name more than a dozen lonely senile people whom he had befriended and ten families where a mentally disturbed person was causing serious distress to the household. The regular visiting and friendly advice offered by the City Mission was very much appreciated. As with the C.A.B. and L.A.B., the value of a continuous friendly relationship with someone outside the immediate family was very evident. The main aim and function of the City Mission is evangelistic, and the Missioners visit homes primarily to read the Bible and discuss religious matters. But their work inevitably involves them in general as well as spiritual welfare. Their work lies mainly with the elderly and with housewives. No young male schizophrenic was included in the Missioner's list of contacts.

Welfare services

While it is convenient to discuss welfare services under the headings of 'statutory' and 'voluntary', in the minds of people receiving them they are divided into 'the people you go to' and 'the people who come to you'. These are sub-divided into 'the people you can see if you like' and, 'the people you have to see whether you like it or not'.

In 1930 the L.C.C. took over the office for the Welfare of the Homeless from the Board of Guardians and the M.A.B.[1] The work began with the unemployed who slept out on the Embankment—the 'office' was at Charing Cross—and was continued under the old Poor Law regulations. Under the National Assistance Act of 1948, which buried so many remnants of the Poor Law, the National Assistance Board

---

[1] Metropolitan Asylum Board.

began to pay half the cost of maintaining the office, the remainder being met by the County Council. It was one of the few places at which the young male schizophrenic was a familiar caller. In spite of this, only two of the survey patients had come to the notice of the people there, though another four might well have done. Of these four, two were eventually arrested by the police because of wandering and drunkenness, and finally received short prison sentences, one for petty pilfering while drunk and the other for disturbing the peace. Both had been shut out from their temporary lodgings and were wandering in East London. They alternated between a settled way of life with a permanent address, and short phases of wandering—they were not habitual tramps and showed no signs of wishing to be, though both slept out during 'bad times'.

The other two who might well have been dealt with by the Welfare Department also slept out on occasions but neither drank. One was overwhelmed with a sudden feeling of panic when discharged from hospital, and fearing that he would damage the room in which he had found lodging, he spent six weeks sleeping in a hole on a bombed site, occasionally buying food with money he had saved while in hospital. 'I stayed there till I came to my senses,' he said. 'At first there was another fellow in the same place, but he went off after a day or two and I had it to myself. In the beginning when I was trying to find somewhere to sleep out the police kept moving me on, but then I found this other bombed place and nobody came near me, except my friend, who came along most evenings to see if I was all right and to try and persuade me to go back to some lodgings. I had to let it all settle in my head you see—the excitement sort of comes up and swamps me and I break loose. I had to let things slow down.'

The second man, when he 'started a bad patch' ceased to go to work and made his way from one set of friends or relatives to another, borrowing money, losing it and giving it away, only to return asking for more. At such times he forgot to pay his rent and so sometimes lost his room in the lodging house when he was least capable of finding and paying for a new one. His homeless periods usually ended in a return to hospital via the police station.

The Welfare Department who maintain the office help not only the vagrant or semi-vagrant among the mentally ill, the neurotic, the epileptic and the physically handicapped; they also help families who have been evicted and families or individuals who have come to London from the provinces without fully appreciating the difficulties they may face in finding work, food, and particularly accommodation.

The men calling at the office are given a chit for a night's lodging at a Salvation Army Hostel, a Rowton House or similar establishment. After this, if necessary, they are helped to obtain clothes, a meal and work, and are put directly in touch with other organizations or authorities. For example, when Mr. Harris was referred to the department, he was advised to get in touch with a particular officer in the British Legion and was given his fare and a note of introduction, after an appointment had been arranged by the Welfare Officer over the phone. This is a small but typical illustration of the immediate personal attention which is given by the Welfare Department and which is of such value to those patients who have begun to wander and lose all their regular 'holds' on the community.

Since the 'clients' come to the department mainly because they have no regular way of life, the officers must do something while the caller is on the premises. People in other social services will only accept immediate requests from an officer who has built up a reputation for goodwill, good judgement and fair dealing. Long delays or lack of co-operation would bring the work of the Welfare Department to an immediate halt. They have, therefore, found ways of giving the immediate personal attention and practical help which is the first need of homeless schizophrenics. As a result, while this department does not provide long-term support, it does help some people to settle down and make their own way again. It also maintains brief but appreciated contact with men who return at intervals over many years as they pass through London while 'going for a ramble'.

The Home Help Service

The Home Help Service is run by the Medical Officer of the London County Council. The service is offered (at 3s. an hour if the recipient can afford to pay, otherwise at a reduced charge or free) to women having babies; to families where the mother is absent through illness, desertion or death, if there are children of school age in the home; to the acutely ill in a temporary crisis; to the aged chronic sick and blind; to very large families where the mother is overwhelmed; and temporarily to widowers or people in special difficulties. The majority of the mentally sick who are helped are senile patients.

The office which deals with the borough has approximately 90 home helps employed in serving 670 households a week. Between 30 and 40 of the householders are mentally sick, the majority being senile. A few are paranoid schizophrenic patients or psychopathic housewives.

A special service is available to people who by reason of mental illness or special disturbances are unable to run their homes. Six of the home helps were specially trained for this work. At the time of the survey four of them were working in the area, one of them with an ex-mental patient who had suicidal tendencies. The scheme has worked well. The down-to-earth common sense brought into the home by these women was invaluable. By contrast, professionally trained workers from a different social class were often received with hostility.

While the home helps were extremely tolerant towards women who had broken down completely, they were much less so towards young mentally sick women who were not obviously helpless. Just as the applicant at the Employment Exchange or Assistance Board who best fitted the officer's idea of a 'deserving case' received the most sympathetic attention, so the person was best off who appealed most deeply to the home help's emotions. The wives of mentally sick husbands, faced with caring for children, going out to work and visiting the hospital at week-ends, did not attract immediate sympathy, though women with crippled husbands at home, or with physically sick husbands in hospital were treated with great kindness.[1]

The home help workers were, like the others we have mentioned, willing to tolerate eccentric and difficult behaviour on the part of old people who were mentally ill. They might complain to the organizer; they rarely refused to continue visiting. It was sometimes not easy for them. One old lady insisted that the neighbours used heavy machinery to shift their furniture and that this kept her awake at night. In an argument about this the home help was dumbfounded by the reply, 'Stands to reason they switch it on at night. Who wants to get out of bed to shift furniture?' Other patients tried to persuade home helps to stop neighbours whom they accused of stealing, abuse, noise or poisoning. Fears of contamination from shared taps and lavatories put extra work on other home helps who humoured their elderly clients by performing certain rituals to make things 'safe'. Incontinence, drunkenness and threats of suicide were treated with much less sympathy.

The maps kept by the organizer showed that the need for home helps was heavily concentrated in particular areas where there was a high turnover of population without local contacts.

The Family Service Unit

The Family Service Unit is situated within the borough but also serves three adjacent boroughs. Its aim is to maintain a long-term relationship with disturbed families. Contact is kept with each family for at least three years. At any one time the Unit is dealing with approximately 60 families. Out of 50 families in contact with the Unit at the time of the inter-

[1] See Appendix 3, pp. 177–178.

view, seven lived in the survey area. Once again it was difficult to find a family where the parents were born and bred in the borough. Four out of the seven were immigrants. Only three of the survey patients were known to the Family Service Unit.

Families were referred to the Unit by the care committee, the probation service, hospital almoners, social workers and the co-ordinating committee for local health and welfare services. Because of the co-ordinating committee's preoccupation with rent arrears and families with school-age children, the F.S.U. staff of six, plus ten voluntary helpers, are fully occupied with the 'socially inadequate'. Psychotic patients of the type admitted to hospital do not form a significant proportion of the numbers looked after by the Unit. The members of the Unit were more apt to recognize as mentally ill those with delusions and flamboyant behaviour who made their fantasies obvious by talking about them. The sickness of depressive patients was not understood in the same way.

The help offered by the Unit is not primarily financial and it is offered to families rather than to isolated individuals. It is based on advice and discussion, practical assistance, and a relationship through which the family can develop a different attitude to life. Children come to the Unit for play and are linked with helpers who take a personal interest in them. Mothers are helped with the household budget and with practical housework, while rent, insurance, employment and other family problems are also discussed with the fathers.

The Family Welfare Association

Unlike the F.S.U. this Association does offer financial help and does deal with individual clients as well as families. The areas covered by the Association's offices are wider than those of the F.S.U.; the survey borough, for example, comes under the jurisdiction of the Area 4 office which also covers Finsbury, Holborn and St. Pancras as well as East

London. Three family social workers are centred on the
office in Myddleton Square, E.C.1, and also the area secretary and an administrative officer. Four part-time workers
deal with general office work and callers.

A quotation from the Association's 1958–59 Annual
Report for Area 4 indicates the nature of the problem facing
such organizations and also the kind of work undertaken:

'The problems with which we are faced are: (1) How
should we develop our work and what should we choose to
do in view of the enormous volume to be done? Should
we become primarily a consultative service for other
agencies dealing with difficult family situations, in view of
the shortage of professionally trained case-workers? (2) If
we continue to work direct with clients and families, how
do we choose them? Do we just take whoever comes, provided a case-work service is needed, or do we try to concentrate on particular groups of problems—mental problems, parent-child difficulties, socially isolated people, for
instance? Or could we restrict our case-load by taking cases
only from certain other agencies such as the medical services, National Assistance Board, Mental Health Workers,
Housing Departments?

'Our Service is one of private office or home interview
for families and individuals who are in difficulties, and co-
operation with other agencies so as to help them. The
object is to assist people living locally who want such
assistance. . . . The trends of the work seem to be develop-
ing very much along two lines. (*a*) Helping couples with
serious marriage difficulties. (*b*) Helping individuals who
are suffering from mental over-strain which may lead to
mental illness.'

Clients were referred to the Association from no less than
75 different sources. Liaison with other agencies is also
close, but neither the volume of work undertaken nor the
level of liaison maintained is evenly distributed. In particular, as might be expected, the Association deals with a larger
proportion of the population of the boroughs near its office

than of those in the East End, which are further away. In the year ending 31st March 1959, the Association was in touch with 14.0 people for every 10,000 from St. Pancras, for example, compared with 6.8 for every 10,000 from the survey borough. None of the survey patients figured among those seen by the F.W.A. from the borough, though neurotic patients from psychiatric out-patients' departments in the borough were well known. In theory the F.W.A. might well deal with many psychotics but in practice they do not. Like the community P.S.W.s, the F.W.A. tends to attract and choose clients who suffer from emotional disturbances in their personalities rather than those in the throes of a total mental disorder which might be classified as a psychotic illness. Since it is almost entirely members of the latter group who are admitted to Long Grove Hospital from the survey borough, it is not surprising to find once again little or no overlap between F.W.A. clients and the survey patients.

The Settlements

The Settlements in East London mostly owe their origin to University and religious bodies which established them at the turn of the century. They are well known to the local community and have a long-standing relationship with it. Each Settlement draws for the most part on the streets immediately surrounding the building for its members, and has its own special reputation. In the borough one is known for its community centre, another for its work with mothers and young children, a third for its old people's centre and a fourth for its youth work.

Only one Settlement takes a specific interest in the mentally ill and ex-mental hospital patients. A patients' club of one type or another has been held there for many years. The present group began some five years ago. Ex-patients and their friends and relatives meet every week for discussion and friendly social activities. It is mainly ex-patients residing in the borough who attend, though some members come from elsewhere. However, only eight of the survey patients are members of the club. This Settlement also caters for a large number of teenagers and young people in its clubs and has an old people's club, women's meetings and acts as 'host' for the Legal Advice Bureau and various other groups.

A second Settlement nearby offers special amenities for the elderly senile patients as part of its general work with the aged. A large number of students and other people engaged in professional work 'live in' during term time and help to run the various activities in the house. The youth clubs in particular are helped by the residents. Holiday schemes for children and mothers are arranged and also home visiting of the elderly. A club for educationally sub-normal girls meets there and a number of other activities are organized by the staff. Apart from the senile patients in the day centre, the only other link with the mentally sick is through the callers at the Citizens' Advice Bureau, which is housed in the Settlement.

At the other end of the borough, close to one of the neighbourhoods which has the highest admission rates for mental illness, stands another Settlement. But the work is mainly focused on mothers and young children and very little is done for the mentally sick. Like the other Settlements, it has an old people's club and also receives a certain number of senile or confused elderly folk. The Save the Children Fund junior club is also housed here and they have a nursery and a young mothers' club.

A fourth Settlement has no specific club or group for the mentally sick, but appears even so to deal with a large number. Approximately a dozen patients keep in touch. Local families draw members of the staff in as friendly counsellors or as people 'who would know about this kind of thing'. The staff thus become mediators between official bodies and the local people, interpreting regulations, explaining rights and obligations and helping the family members to adapt to or manipulate the bureaucratic system as best they could. The relatives of a mentally sick person, finding themselves in a state of conflict over the patient, sometimes came to 'talk it over' at the house. One woman found herself torn between duty to her sister or her duty to her husband. 'She is my own sister but I have to think of my husband.' Another woman whose mother was demented could not bring herself to arrange for her mother to go to hospital, but explained to a member of the Settlement staff, 'My old man will leave home if this goes on much longer. What can I do?'

It is precisely this type of informal, personal, familiar relationship which the relatives seek. An impartial person, known and readily available, who has no power to act, but can only discuss and advise, is a kind of person that local families sometimes need.

In this chapter some of the services and organizations for mental patients in the survey area have been discussed and described. Few of them are specifically arranged for the psychotic. The psychotic is nobody's special business. He is the responsibility of many different people whom he must get to know just at the time when his ability to do so is most impaired. Many of the services offered do not quite meet his needs. He is liable to become bewildered and feel that society and even social services are organized against him.

Some people with problems remained quite out of touch with the social services, while another group of people with very similar problems attracted widespread attention. Of the 27 patients who had received help, 18 were known to almost all the welfare agencies in the district. Mrs. Hearne is known to the local hospitals, two out-patient clinics, the Care Committee, the Citizens' Advice Bureau, the Community Psychiatric Social Worker, the Long Grove Social Workers, two Settlements, the British Legion, the Police, the Court Missionary, the Priory and the W.V.S. No doubt others could be added to the list. Similarly Mrs. Mayerat and her family are known to the Welfare Department, the housing departments of the borough and the L.C.C., the probation officer, members of Alcoholics Anonymous and Neurotics Nomine. Mr. Mace is well known to the office of the D.A.O. (Duly Authorized Officer), to the social workers and to Rowton Houses in neighbouring boroughs. Miss Maxted is known at eight different hospitals, and her family are visited by the Chest Clinic almoners, the borough welfare officers and the housing officers, among many others.

Just as certain street names are notorious to those who plot the distribution of mental illness, so the mention of certain family names in any welfare office will evoke an immediate response. One relative was very much aware of this. 'Once you get known you're a marked man. You never start square anywhere. They got files as big as that on me at *all* the offices and if I go somewhere for something quite different they nip out of the office, ring up some other office and say, "I got Mr. So-and-so here—is anything known about his family?", and I tell you they come back looking quite different, and pass you on to some other officer, and it starts all over again. Then they start calling. Me and my wife we've had a basinful. We've had everybody call here, practically, from the Prime Minister down. I just got made into a case—I don't want to be, but my family are known all round the offices.'

He went on to explain that being called on and having a file at all the offices would not be so bad if it bore fruit, but from his point of view it only resulted in one authority after another needlessly recording his history all over again. This complaint was not uncommon. With the best will in the world welfare officers and social workers cannot offer mental patients facilities which do not exist, but they could perhaps do more to maintain continuity and consistency in those services which there are.

As long ago as 1939 the Chief Officer of Public Assistance was pleading for the reduction in the multiplicity of services. 'The multiplication of the social services is resulting in a growing bewilderment to the ordinary needy person.

He finds himself lost in a maze of new laws, new regulations, new organizations and new officials, and sorely in need of a trustworthy guide. The Poor Law is a general service which supplements the categorical social services both by filling up the gaps which they leave, and often by acting more quickly and freely. A Relieving Officer, therefore, often finds himself as a co-ordinating factor, or indeed as a focus for the specialist services when he is dealing with the un-discriminated needs of a poor family.'[1]

The Welfare State has done away with the Relieving Officer, but from the point of view of some mental patients at least, there is a need for some such person who could be both a guide to specialist services and an understanding listener. The sorest social need of the psychotic is for one trustworthy guide.

[1] Bligh, E. C., *L.C.C. Handbook for Relieving Officers.*

XI

IN CONCLUSION:
CONTINUITY OF CARE AND
MENTAL HEALTH

IN the last three chapters the many diverse social services
have been reviewed, both statutory and voluntary, which
are, at least in theory, available to the mental patient in
this district. It is not a comforting picture. The people who
work in them are generally trying in every way they can to
help the patients who have figured in this book. But there
are too many under-staffed agencies, insufficiently co-
ordinated, dealing with the mentally sick in a fragmentary
way, and too few consistently offering an all-embracing
service for the psychotic patient.

The services are confusing to describe and to understand;
how much more so to the patients and harassed relatives
who have to use them. They want something straight-
forward, but they are faced with a formidable bureaucratic
structure which would tax the understanding of the sanest
and most competent person.

This summary has been based on interviews with officials
of these organizations in 1960 and with patients in 1958
and 1959. It is therefore a composite picture of the situation
in one small area of England before the new Mental Health
Act of 1959 had taken effect.

How should it take effect? By what means could local
authorities and hospitals put its generous intent in practice?
These questions are now widely debated. The new Act is
both a new beginning and an opportunity.

1. *A unified service.* The confusion is so obvious that it is barely necessary to plead for some rationalization in the existing hugger-mugger of services. The difficulties are considerable, but such rationalization should result in the mentally sick person being able to turn to one official rather than to many. Every split in the existing services adds to the number of people who may have access to the patient and his family.

The re-alignment of medical services under the 1946 Act transferred the mental hospitals from local government to Ministry of Health; the 1959 Mental Health Act leaves prevention and after-care as the province of the local authorities. The traditional tension between the medical profession and local government has already been described by Dr. Galloway.[1] Since the tendency is for patients to stay for shorter periods in mental hospitals and return home to complete their treatments, or spend several periods 'on leave' before finally returning home, lack of communication between hospital and local government, with all the conflicting advice and changes of contact it implies, adds seriously to the problems of the mental patient.

Some of the tensions between local authority and hospital centre around which type of case is rightly the concern of each. For many years the hospital has had to receive the patients sent to it, and those patients admitted from the East London catchment area are almost entirely psychotic, with a strong proportion of regressed psychotics. But the work of the local authority has been geared more to the needs of the neurotic.

Historically, this has come about in two main ways. Psychotics have generally been retained in hospital to such an extent in the past that there has been little pressure to evolve methods of social rehabilitation for them. And secondly the general interest in Freudian psychiatry and its implications for social welfare have led to the slanting of

---

[1] Galloway, J. F. 'Integration of Preventive and Curative Health Services through comprehensive local administrative Units'.

many schemes and social welfare services in the direction
of the neurotic. The dislike of the chronic psychotic has
not been lessened by the failure of therapeutic measures
applicable to neurotics when used uncritically with psychotics.

In February 1958, in the Maudsley lecture given to the
Royal Medico-Psychological Association, Dr. Duncan Macmillan still felt that, 'Most of the community schemes do not
cope with all forms of psychiatric illness. For instance,
patients with chronic psychoses, particularly if they have
anti-social reactions, are usually sent to the local mental
hospital and pass from the care of the community service.
Some schemes are more comprehensive, but generally speaking the chronic mental patient is excluded from community
treatment once the home situation becomes too strained for
him to go on living at home.'[1]

The separation of the various aspects of the service
offered to the mentally ill therefore results in a situation
where there is no clear line of continuity between develop-
ing a psychotic illness, recognizing it as illness, getting help
in obtaining the relevant treatment, readjusting to everyday life and obtaining after-care.

It is not easy to bridge this gap between the two bureau-
cracies. But it is clear that unless it is bridged, little solid
progress will be made with community mental health. That
it *can* be done is shown by Nottingham where Dr. Macmillan
himself has played a central part in an impressive experiment. He holds two key posts: he is Superintendent of
Mapperley Hospital and also Medical Officer of Mental
Health for the city. He is responsible not only for the
hospital but also for education of the public, for prevention,
and for all domiciliary and community care of all the
mentally defective and disordered people in the district.
'The organization of mental health care in Nottingham is
based on integration with the mental health department of
the local health authority, and an intensive system of out-

[1] Macmillan, D., 'Mental Health Services of Nottingham'.

patient clinics. The policy is one of short-term admission to hospital with the long-term care of the patients carried out on a domiciliary and out-patient basis.'[1] From all this has resulted a general exchange of experience and understanding—social workers for the city visit the wards regularly, nurses accompany social workers into the homes, a psychiatrist and a social worker jointly visit people before they are admitted to hospital.

The Nottingham solution cannot be rigidly applied elsewhere, especially in much larger cities like London. But the general idea, of linking up what has previously been separate, is undoubtedly sound. The more that co-operation on these lines can be achieved elsewhere, the better will some of the least fortunate members of our society be looked after.

2. *Recognizing the local way of life.* The future service will also be successful only if it is sensitive to the nature of local society. For locally-born people in this part of London— the immigrants are another story—this means being sensitive above all to the kind of families to which they belong. An earlier book gave many examples of family influence:

> 'When the wife gets contradictory advice from the welfare clinic and from her Mum she usually listens to the person she trusts most. . . ."I take more notice of my Mum than I do of the welfare. She's had eight and we're all right. Experience speaks for itself, more or less, doesn't it? If you're living near your mother, you don't really need that advice. You've got more confidence in your mother than you would have in the advice they'd give you." '

Such families are liable to be at odds with authority, and do everything possible to shield members with mental or other troubles from outside influence.

But obviously individual families cannot be self-sufficient. They sometimes need the social services even if they are frightened of them. So what do they do in time of trouble?

[1] Macmillan, D., op cit.

They do not normally brave bureaucracy in its office; instead, they turn to an intermediary, one of the local 'Cognoscenti'[1] who seem to know what to do in an emergency. He or she may be the local publican, the secretary of the darts clubs, on the staff of a Settlement, or a neighbour—someone anyway who 'knows his way around'. Mr. Blanchard, for example, approached the manager of his public house and explained very hesitantly that his wife had been 'acting a little strange' for a long time now and he was afraid to go back to work and leave her in the house alone. He himself was, he said, at 'his wit's end' too, but on no account would he ever consider 'putting his wife away'. The manager, with Mr. Blanchard's permission, approached a resident in a local Settlement and arranged a meeting over a beer in his pub. There arrangements were made for a neighbour to begin taking Mrs. Blanchard to the psychiatric out-patients' clinic.

The mental health service should clearly seek to make use of key people like these in the borough, who will continue to carry weight with entrenched local families in a way open to very few social workers, and who could therefore be of immense value. What is necessary is not that they should be supplanted but supplied with more, and more reliable, information than they have at present about the service.

If, as Zilboorg[2] contends, the expression of mental illness is limited to the range of problems which are culturally characteristic for the individual, then any mental health treatment programme moving towards community care must take account of the nature of the culture from which the mentally sick evolved their particular modes of social expression. Each community requires a psychiatric service which is either fitted directly to its particular cultural needs, or at least not framed in terms which inevitably make it

---

[1] I have used this term to describe members of the local community who are particularly respected as sources of information.

[2] Zilboorg, G., *A History of Medical Psychiatry*.

totally unacceptable to the individual from that community. Otherwise, no amount of pleading will persuade him that the hospital can offer him anything approaching the standard of help and protection offered by the familiar place in a strongly united kinship group.

The members of voluntary organizations who live locally are often able to develop a fuller understanding of the local way of life than other workers and to build up stronger ties with the people in the district. It is therefore all the more important that they should themselves be convinced of the goodwill and efficiency of the hospital.

The members of voluntary organizations also contribute to some of the discontinuities mentioned in the previous section, since they often find themselves opposed to statutory bodies in decisions concerning the mentally sick person and his relatives. While it is perhaps important to retain checks and balances upon the total powers of state bodies, yet such disagreements add sadly to the bewilderment of the mental patients. On the other hand, the statutory bodies should receive more information and training about mental patients so that they can adjust their attitudes to who does and who does not truly qualify for help by reason of a very real, if not always immediately obvious, disability.

The importance of 'public relations' is one of the lessons of the experiment at Worthing, where an effort was made, and successfully, to get people to attend a 'day hospital' for early treatment. The doctor in charge has said that:

> 'The success of a district mental health service depends on its public having learnt to accept mental illness as it would any other illness and to seek advice and treatment promptly. In this respect, West Sussex is probably better off than many other parts of the country. For some years frequent talks, followed by visits to the hospital, have been given to many groups of people and psychiatry and the mental hospital is no longer a mystery.'[1]

[1] Carse, J., 'A District Mental Health Service'.

Any campaign of popular education should in a district like this be directed in the first place at the people I have called the Cognoscenti.

Similarly, the dissemination of information about what happens to the patient after he has entered hospital might help to dispel some of the grosser 'Snake Pit' fantasies which still circulate in the neighbourhood, while a clear indication of the sources of help after discharge from hospital could be further emphasized. However, clinging to fantasies about the hospital would appear to be directly connected with the patient's desire to remain responsible for himself. Since much of the confusion about entry to hospital is also a result of the desire not to know about such things, the dissemination of correct information alone will be of little avail until a sufficient number of patients return home, or receive treatment in the community, in a way which makes it obvious that they have not been treated as socially inadequate and totally irresponsible.

If the social aspects of mental illness are to be adequately dealt with and community care increased, then the cultures in the catchment area need to be well understood. The nature of the sick person's behaviour, the course of his illness and the outcome of treatment cannot be usefully measured in isolation from his culture. Is this or that element in his behaviour part of his illness or a culturally conditioned response to the situation he experiences in hospital? What rehabilitation scheme would prove most acceptable to an East London man? Until the people in the community are aware of the true nature of the hospital, and the hospital aware of the nature of the way of life and values in the community, neither can use the other to the best advantage of the sick.

In order to teach social adaptation to the consequences of psychotic illness the hospital must first learn from the community how to translate the language of psychiatry into the local language. As Dr. A. B. Monro has pointed out in his article, 'A concept of Mental Health obtained by

Comparing a Normal and a Disordered Population',[1] based
on a comparison of the cultural trait scores for 200 mental
patients and 208 American Servicemen, a balanced state of
mental health is achieved by those whose emotional expression is 'firmly controlled and canalized by social considera-
tions'. He concludes that therapeutic techniques facilitating
the achievement of mental health would be educational in
nature. 'Consideration of the problem brings out the strong
suggestion that the appropriate techniques would be educational rather than strictly medical, a conclusion reinforced
by similar thought about the other groups. The evidence
under scrutiny therefore supports those psychiatrists and
psychologists who contend that education must be one of
our most powerful agencies in promoting mental health.'
A further study[2] by Dr. Monro of behaviour patterns in
mental disorder re-emphasized the significance of social
factors in psychiatry. Thus studies and research techniques
widely varying in nature and origin have confirmed the use-
fulness and significance of the present concern with the
social elements in the origin, expression and rehabilitation
of mental illness.

'The new aim is to make the hospital a school for social
learning where the psychotic, discarded by society as a
whole, may gradually re-acquire social skills and techniques
sufficient to allow him to emerge again or to live at as high
a level as possible within the therapeutic community.'[3]
Under the new Mental Health Act, with its emphasis on
community care, it would seem that education in social
learning needs to move out of 'school' and be continued
'on the job' in society. This is the greatest challenge to the
skills of the mental hospital.

3. *Making use of patients' groups.* There are places in the
borough—in parks, public gardens, churchyards, bombed

---

[1] Monro, A. B., 'A concept of Mental Health obtained by Comparing a Normal
and a Disordered Population'.

[2] Monro, A. B., 'Behaviour Patterns in Mental Disorder'.

[3] Carstairs, G. M., *et al.*, 'Occupational Treatment of Chronic Psychotics'. See
Appendix 3 for note on experimental schemes in hospitals.

sites, a low wall near a bus-stop, or a corner seat near a road junction—where one sees little groups of mentally sick people and their friends together. Some of them were former patients of Long Grove; others had never been near a mental hospital, but still felt an affinity with the group. Sometimes unexpected combinations of schizophrenic, defective and elderly confused patients walk slowly together along the street. When one of them is feeling bad, the group walks almost in single file, a little apart from the sick person. The group will put up with, and even protect, any member as long as he does not begin to rave or otherwise attract public action, when they will walk off or even drive him away.

The members sometimes offer help to each other. Molly went with Christine to get her a job. George's wife knitted Henry a pullover; Henry bought the wool himself. Cigarettes, tobacco, and sometimes food are scrupulously shared. When Jimmy took Alan to his room, 'We had a regular soup up, he needs it, he doesn't feed himself properly.' 'If one of us is down on his luck,' said Alan, 'the rest will stump up somehow. Anyone who doesn't join in will be shut off by the rest. They don't want to know him.'

The patients' groups are rarely of both sexes, by their own choice. Only one women's group was discovered, which met in Mrs. Hearne's kitchen. Her mother had been worried because Molly Hearne used to wander about in the dark when she went out to visit her friends, and said to her, 'If you want to see your friends, you bring them round here.' The women make tea and chat together while the mother keeps order and enjoys the conversation. Not being able to go out, and being a sociable person, she takes quite a pleasure in her daughter's unofficial 'club' and the patients seem to enjoy it too. Mrs. Hearne rattled off the names of a dozen or more patients who visit the house from time to time, though only four or five are regular callers. In these groups, the patient can talk about his illness without people moving away or trying to prevent him. He can express bizarre or illogical ideas without fearing they will be foreign to his audience. He experiences a feeling of relief and assurance when he finds out there *are* other people who have similar ideas, or at least are open to believe such things possible, and above all they treat him as a person whose opinion can be respected.

The majority of the members of these groups are eager to avoid official welfare. They are suspicious because they have found that it is bought at the price of conformity to some outside standard. If 'they' are aware of your existence there is always the danger that 'they' will get you back into hospital 'for your own good' or into some institution; or 'they' will try to alter your way of life. The older patients in particular can remember the heyday of welfare organizations in the East End and refer with irony to one they call 'Cringe or Starve'. By contrast, gifts within the group carry no more than the expectation of a return from a member when help is needed. The group will not 'put him away' nor ask him to attend a church nor to conform to any standard other than that of mutual aid.

It is possible to make contact with these spontaneous groups, and the mental health service could do so in the future, provided it is done with tact and without any ill-advised effort to impose 'order' upon the members. If some help were given to them, especially by providing a room where the groups could meet at night or in wet weather, they could be even more valuable in linking people who might otherwise be alone to each other and to society.

4. *Sheltered workshops.* Many patients have expressed the desire for a sheltered workshop: many of their problems on returning to the community are connected with finding and keeping 'a steady job'. This would act as a rehabilitation centre for those capable of ordinary employment and as a regular means of employment for those who were not. Experience at Waddon and Kidbrooke rehabilitation centres and in such hospitals as Banstead and Netherne (to name only two with large 'hospital factories') has shown that many

patients who have been ill for long periods of time are quite capable of working, given the right surroundings and supervision. Bristol has opened a factory in the community solely for the employment of ex-patients. It is something which is required generally.

Other needs could be met by the provision of foster homes for those without friends or relatives; more day centres[1] for those unfit for work, living with relatives and requiring treatment and occupation during the day; more 'night hospitals' for those who can work by day, but who need some treatment and have proved to be particularly difficult at night-time while at home; and clubs and advice centres to which both patients and relatives could have access.

5. *Bringing hospital to the patients.* A major obstacle to an integrated mental health service lies in local antipathy to the mental hospital. Although this shows signs of improvement, it is still strong enough to prevent the mentally sick or their relatives from seeking help in the early stages of illness, when help could most easily and effectively be given. The hospital cannot logically be blamed for failing to do what it is prevented from attempting. Yet all too often community prejudice is strengthened by the return of a self-discharged psychotic who went to hospital after many years of illness and returned 'no better'. In some the hostility to hospital makes them oppose admission until the last stages of regression.

In the long run only an obviously high standard of service from the hospital, acceptable to the local people, will defeat prejudice. However, some things can help in altering rigid opinions in the community. Domiciliary visiting more than once before admission can be very helpful. 'The encounter with the hospital doctor in the security of the patient's home will often provide the link enabling the patient to move from one social milieu to another. In many cases

[1] There are more than 40 day centres now operating in this country for the mentally sick and several 'night hospitals'.

"certification" has resulted largely from the fear, and conse-
quent refusal to accept treatment, engendered by the
patient's handling.'[1]

One of the chief difficulties in dispersing antipathy and
establishing an accurate picture of the hospital is that it is
not easily visible to the local population. The policy of the
nineteenth and early twentieth century was to build
hospitals at a distance from the urban populations they
served. Since Long Grove is so far from East London not
only do relatives find visiting difficult, but lurid miscon-
ceptions of the hospital also easily become accepted. The
distance must seem all the greater to people from the
borough because, on the whole, they are used to living the
greater part of their lives locally.

> 'Another man, in a letter asking for help in getting another
> home, wrote, "I am not particular where you send me, the
> further the better. I do not mind if it is as far as Old Ford as
> I have left my wife and wish to keep as far away as possible."
> Old Ford is five minutes' walk from his wife.'[2]

Such an attitude is not uncommon.

Patients used to their familiar street and the quarter mile
in each direction round it, upon being brought to Epsom
by ambulance, feel that they have lost all hope of contact
with home and are seriously confused by the strangeness of
the hospital and the countryside. One such patient said, 'I
feel frightened down there. It's so empty. There's no streets
or nothing and you can't go and look in the shop windows
with the lights on after dark and make yourself feel less
lonely.' Equally, though they staff the out-patients clinics,
the psychiatrists are, on the whole, also cut off from the
community, and lack opportunities to become familiar with
the background of their patients. The significance of neighbourhoods which mean so much to the patients is lost and

---

[1] Leigh, D., 'Schizophrenia in General Practice'.
[2] Young, M., and Willmott, P., op. cit., p. 87.

the doctor cannot use common knowledge of familiar places to help establish an easy relationship.

At such a distance it is difficult to make rehabilitation gradual, difficult for the patient to begin work or to visit his home while still sleeping in the hospital and receiving treatment. Even taking groups of patients to visit the borough before they come out needs considerable time, money, and ill-spared staff. Similarly, local groups wishing to visit the hospital regularly find the journey more than they can manage. For all these reasons it would help enormously if a mental hospital, very much smaller than the old, could be provided very much nearer to the district from which the patients come. This would also help to bring the hospital and the community services together.

These are but five steps that might be taken. Between them they could accomplish much. But perhaps more important than the type of administration is the spirit which informs it.

A mental patient is a man or woman struggling to maintain a meaningful life in the face of a bewildering and sometimes crushing disability. His family, his doctor, the nurses, social workers and psychiatrists see only certain aspects of a problem which to him is indivisible. Unless they coordinate their help, and offer it to the mentally ill person in a way which he can accept, their efforts will be frustrated. Treatment must discriminate between the illness and the person who is ill. In physical illness the futility of remedies to which the patient is allergic is recognized. It must be as clearly admitted that in the treatment of mental disorders methods should be used in environments and under circumstances which do not undermine the patient's confidence, responsibility, and self-respect.

I will end with the advice of Mr. Kerstein, who was one of the many remarkable and admirable people interviewed in the course of this study. 'The best kind of relationship is what you'd call fatherly care—like a father to a son or a brother to a brother.' He suggested that this could only come about where the patient was treated as an individual, recognizing that the loss of individuality was forced on him by the hospital as an institution. 'The solution is to split the hospital into small units. And you need a lot more religion, more kindness and more fatherly care. Then you'd get people recommending other patients to go into hospital. Well, it's like a business. You can't ask fairer than that—one person recommending another to go to hospital, can you?'

APPENDIX 1

Interview Schedule

Subject	Informant	Serial No.
Name	Name	
Address	Address	
OP	Relationship to subject	
LG	Those present	
XLG		

---

1. Present household

	Name	Rel. to Subj.	Sex	Age	Marital Status	House-hold	Dwelling
1 Subject							
2–10							

---

2. Household before last admission for treatment

	Name	Rel. to Subj.	Sex	Age	Marital Status	House-hold	Dwelling
1 Subject							
2–10							

---

3. a) Housing

Type of dwelling

No. of rooms Fixed bath Shared WC Shared tap Shared cooking facilities

---

b) Birthplace   Length of residence in borough

c) Type of education Age left school

d) Religion   Subject   Spouse   Attendance at church?

159

e) Work

Subject	Spouse
Present occupation (if any)	1. Full time
Occupation prior to admission	2. Part time
If unemployed prior to admission length of unemployment	3. Not working
How many jobs has X had during the last three years?	
Were some of the household dependent on X's earnings?	
Was he able to support himself while at home?	
Did he have any difficulty getting a job on returning home?	

---

4. Hospital history

a) Date admitted (in or O.P.)   Length of stay
1–6

b) Reason for leaving
Discharged by hospital or self?
What led to discharge?

Subject's Schedule

1. Do you feel going to hospital has helped you?

2. How did you come to go to hospital in the first place?

3. Did you go to your own doctor first? (Explore initiation of contact with doctor and hospital.)

4. Did you have any special worry at home just before you went to hospital?

5. *a*) How did you feel about going to hospital? (Explore attitudes to in- or out-patient experience.)

   b) (Short term patients) How was it that you came home again so soon?

   c) What did you think it would be like before you'd been to the hospital?

6. Did any difficulties crop up?

   a) In hospital

   b) Out of hospital

7. What do you think is the best way to deal with your trouble?
   Need rest
   Need treatment
   Best at home
   Best in hospital

8. Is there anything which you feel should be done to help you, which has not been done?

9. *Do kinship chart*
   Note the following on the chart. Ego, parents and children, ages and occupations, place of residence. Date of parents' death. Ego's age at marriage. Siblings in birth order, place of residence and number of children. Note number of live born. Frequency of contact. Mark for all the above relatives. Mark visiting frequency with capital V and number. Mark relatives with mental or nervous disorders and write in specific illnesses mentioned, such as asthma, T.B., etc. If any special tie is mentioned with an aunt, uncle, nephew, niece or cousin, mark the relative on chart.

10. *a)* Did either of your parents die before you were 15 or separate or get a divorce?
    b) Did your own children grow up at home with both parents till 15 (or till now if under 15)?
    c) Which of the family do you find it easiest to get on with?
    Interview Situation

Subject	Length of interview
Spouse	Completed in one call
Children	Date
Other rels.	
Non-rels.	

Informant's schedule

1. Now I would be glad if you would tell me a little more about X's trouble
   a) How long would you say it is since it really began?
   b) What was it that made you feel he was not himself? (Explore behaviour)
   c) Did you discuss it with anyone?

d) What made you finally decide he must go for treatment?

e) What was the feeling in the family about X going to hospital? (Explore conflicting opinions)

f) Who went with X to go into the observation ward? And to LG?

g) Which members of the family have seen the doctor or hospital authorities each time?

2. Did any special problem or trouble crop up in the family just before X went to hospital? (e.g. sickness, aged relatives, new baby, financial problems, etc.)

3. With which of the family would you say X gets on best?

4. (Short term patients only) I see that X did not stop long in hospital. How was it that he came home again so soon?

5. How do you think he felt about being in hospital?

6. And how did you get on with the hospital?
   Prompt List Family impression

   Is there any difficulty about patient coming back?

   Who suggested return home?

   Have you seen PSW?

7. Now I want to ask you especially about the arrangements which were made when X went into hospital.

   Were you there when the doctor suggested going to Long Grove?

   How was it put to you?

   Were you told anything about the hospital and the system for entering hospital? (e.g. as vol. or non-stat. or cert. patient)

   Were you given a leaflet about the hospital?

   Who told you how to get there and about visiting times?

   What did you think it would be like before you'd been to see the hospital?

   How did you get on the first time?

   Who wrote or took or sent parcels to X?

   Did he write home at all?

8. What do *you* think is the matter with X?

9. Do you think when he's not well he's better in hospital or at home?

10. What do you think is the best way of dealing with this kind of trouble?

11. One of the things I am trying to find out is how families manage when they have someone at home with this trouble. The next few questions are about that.

   Who accepts responsibility for X at home?

   Did you have unusual expense in connexion with his illness?

12. What kind of difficulties cropped up?

   Explore: Personal behaviour in family
           Personal behaviour in neighbourhood
           Helpful in house
           Food problems
           Safe with money?
           Safe alone or with children
           Wouldn't meet people or go out?
           Unable to wash, dress, etc.?
           Silent or excessively talkative?
           Dangerous to self or others?
           Laundry problems because incontinent?
           Housebound?
           Troublesome at night?

13. *a*) What are the things you remember most about X's behaviour just before he went to hospital last time?

   b) Did he do anything which worried you very much?

14. Have you ever talked to the doctor or nurse about X? How did you feel about what they told you?

APPENDIX 2

Additional Statistical Information

p. 4. Details of the 31 patients not interviewed

	Age	Sex	Marital status	Diagnosis
Died	61	M	M	Depression
	51	M	S	Depression
	36	M	S	Anxiety state
	59	F	W	Schizophrenia
	80	M	W	Senile dementia
	69	M	M	Senile depression
	59	F	W	Depression
Suicide	36	M	S	Schizophrenia
	46	M	M	Anxiety state
Moved out of district	26	M	M	Delusional psychosis
	43	F	M	Paranoic schizophrenia
	56	M	M	Depression
	72	F	M	Paranoia
	50	F	M	Paranoia
	78	F	W	Senile psychosis
	53	M	Sep.	G.P.I.
	27	F	S	Schizophrenia
	62	M	M	G.P.I.
Transferred to Old People's Home	72	F	W	Senile psychosis
Untraceable	32	F	M	Depression
	21	M	S	Psychopathy with depression
	25	M	S	Schizophrenia
	49	F	M	Depression
	24	F	M	Schizophrenia
	57	F	S	Depression
	40	F	S	Depression
	78	F	W	Senile psychosis
	33	M	S	Schizophrenia
	37	F	M	Depression
Wanted by police, 'disappeared'	47	M	M sep.	Depressive psychopathy
	32	M	M sep.	Depressive alcoholic
Refused	44	M	S	Anxiety state
	35	F	M	Schizophrenia
	25	M	S	Schizophrenia

Additional Statistical Information

p. 65. The comparison of patients to local population by sex, age, and marital status

TABLE IX shows the patients in each age, sex, and marital status group as a ratio of the corresponding number in the population of the survey borough, each such ratio being divided by the ratio for all men and women respectively. Because the ratios of patients to borough population are identical for men and for women the two sections of this table (male and female) are directly comparable.

TABLE IX

RATIO OF PATIENTS TO THE POPULATION OF SURVEY BOROUGH AGED 15 OR OVER AT CENSUS 1951, BY SEX, AGE AND MARITAL STATUS. (RATIOS MULTIPLIED BY 1,000) *

MEN

Age Group	Single		Married Widowed or Separated†		Total	
15–34	173	(14)	25	(2)	99	(16)
35–64	116	(3)	84	(14)	88	(17)
65 or over	225	(1)	144	(6)	153	(7)
Total	161	(18)	76	(22)	100	(40)

† One man aged 73 was widowed and one aged 48 separated.

WOMEN

Age Group	Single		Married		Widowed or Separated		Total	
15–34	107	(8)	41	(4)	0	(0)	69	(12)
35–64	298	(10)	53	(8)	204	(6)	112	(24)
65 or over	313	(2)	86	(2)	145	(6)	141	(10)
Total	174	(20)	51	(14)	165	(12)	100	(46)

* *Note:* The number of patients on which the ratios are based are shown in brackets.

In the case of both men and women, patients include relatively more single than ever-married persons. There is also a tendency for the patients to be older than the population as a whole.

For each age group, also, the relative number of single exceeds that of ever-married persons; within marital status groups, the trends are not so consistent, but there is a tendency for the older groups to be more represented than the younger. Deviations may well be due to the very small numbers in some of the cells.

p. 6. The tendency for admission rates to rise with age

External figures of admission to all mental hospitals in England and Wales show that the tendency is found for admission rates to rise in old age for the population as a whole (see Table X). These figures also suggest that outside the borough, relatively more women than men become in-patients of a mental hospital. 'It is estimated that on 31st December 1956, of people aged 65 and over, one out of 109 was resident in a mental hospital.'[1]

[1] Brooke, E. M., 'Mental Health and the Population'.

TABLE X

ADMISSION RATES PER 100,000 HOME POPULATION TO ALL MENTAL HOSPITALS, ENGLAND AND WALES, 1956

Age	Men	Women
15–19	66	72
20–24	152	145
25–34	218	248
35–44	212	275
45–54	200	296
55–64	248	334
65–74	277	357
75 or over	338	378

Note: In view of the larger numbers a more detailed age distribution is possible than for the Survey borough table (Table I).

Source: General Register Office: The Registrar General's Statistical Review of England and Wales for the three years 1954–1956, *Supplement on Mental Health*, London: H.M.S.O., 1960.

Inevitably, the question arises whether the difference in age (and for other characteristics) between patients and non-patients is due to the differential admission rates, or to differences in the incidence of mental disease in the population.

The only set of figures which may throw light on this question is obtained from a survey of 106 General Practices conducted jointly by the General Register Office and the College of General Practitioners in 1955–56. This measured *inter alia* the age distribution of all patients who consulted their general practitioner and who were subsequently diagnosed as suffering from a psycho-neurotic or psychotic complaint. Few of the former, but over 30% of the latter, were subsequently admitted to hospitals. The age distribution of the psychotics may therefore be taken as an approximation to the age distribution of those who suffer from a complaint which justifies hospitalization.

Sixty-four per cent of 274 cases diagnosed as psychotics were women, as compared with 59% of total admissions in 1956. The difference is small and may be due to chance. The age distribution, compared with the population, of psychotics consulting their doctor, is shown in Table XI.

TABLE XI

NUMBER OF PATIENTS DIAGNOSED AS PSYCHOTICS PER 100,000 HOME POPULATION 1955–56*

Age	Men	Women
15–44	170	150
45–64	160	300
65 or over	520	930
Total	170	270

* Logan, W. P. D., and Cushion, A. A., *Morbidity Statistics from General Practice.*

Data obtained from the general practitioners' survey are, for many reasons, not directly comparable with figures of hospital admissions. We are not justified therefore in drawing conclusions in detail, but may note any general trend that may emerge. There is little doubt that relatively more old people aged 65 or over suffer from psychotic complaints. In the case of women, there is a consistent trend over the three age groups. There is also a tendency for the diagnosis rates, both for men and for women, to increase more sharply than the admission rates; if true, this would indicate a falling admission rate relative to those in need of hospitalization, but the figures are too tentative to provide conclusive evidence.

p. 6. The diagnostic classification of the patients' sample by marital status, sex, and age

TABLE XIIa

DESCRIPTION OF PATIENTS' SAMPLE

	Married	*Single*	*Separated Widowed or Divorced*
Men	20	18	2
Women	14	20	12
Diagnosis			
Anxiety state	1	2	1
Confusional Psychosis ..	2	1	
Depressive	14	4	4
Hysteria	2	1	
Mania		1	1
Manic Depression ..	1	1	
Paranoia	2	2	2
Parkinson's	2		
Psychotic epileptic ..		1	
Puerperal Depression ..	1		
Schizophrenia	4	23	
Senile psychosis	5	2	6

TABLE XIIb

DESCRIPTION OF PATIENTS' SAMPLE CONTINUED

	19–24	25–29	30–34	35–39	40–44	45–49	50–54	55–59	60–64	65–69	70–74	75–79	80–84
						Age							
Married ..		4	2	2	4	6	4	5	3	2	3	2	
Single ..	6	11	5	3	1	4	2	1	2	3			
Separated, Wid. or Div.						1	1	1	1		4	1	2
Diagnosis													
Anxiety ..		2			1		1						
Conf. Psy. ..								1	1	1			
Depressive ..	1	2	1	1	2	6	3	2	1	1	2		
Hysteria ..		1						1		1			
Mania ..						2							
Man. Dep. ..				1			1						
Paranoia ..		1				1	1	2			1		
Parkinson's ..								1	1				
Psy. epileptic						1							
Puerp. Dep. ..			1										
Schizophrenia	5	9	5	4	1	1	1		1				
Senility ..									2	2	4	3	2

p. 89. Percentage of locally-born and admission rate for schizophrenia

The survey borough has the highest proportion of London-born people in the population of all London boroughs (82%). It also has a lower admission rate for schizophrenia than the following boroughs: Stepney, Shoreditch, Finsbury, Westminster, Kensington, Paddington, Hampstead, St. Marylebone.

This information was provided in a personal communication from the Registrar General's office and is based on research which will be published by the Registrar General at a future date.

p. 86. Admission rates and marital status

The Registrar General suggests that single people are 'over-represented' (see table below) in mental hospital populations because 'it is possible that the numbers of admissions of single persons are inflated by their entering and leaving hospital more frequently than would married or widowed persons, who had a spouse or children to care for them'.[1]

But the picture presented by the survey suggests that the admission pattern is more complicated than this. Married people did come to hospital less frequently and for shorter periods, but many of the young single patients were by no means isolated. However, it was noticeable that the widows who came to hospital mainly lived alone or had no children and the married women who did come to hospital often came following the death of their mother.

While some of the single patients appeared to stay in hospital because they had no one to help them keep out of it, it seems likely that a high proportion of them are in fact more seriously ill than the once-married people who come to hospital. Loss or the lack of significant kin can equally well cause the hospitalization of the married as the single.

TABLE XIII

DIRECT ADMISSIONS BY SEX, AGE AND MARITAL STATUS
PER 100,000 POPULATION AT THE 1951 CENSUS

		Age Groups						
		20—	25—	35—	45—	55—	65—	75+
Males								
Single		16	38	38	35	29	29	30
M. W. Div. . .		5	9	10	12	16	20	29
Females								
Single		16	35	38	36	31	29	40
M. W. Div. . .		9	13	16	19	21	23	31

[1] *Registrar General's Statistical Review of England and Wales* 1950–51. *Supplement on General Morbidity, Cancer and Mental Health*, p. 147.

APPENDIX 3

NOTES ON THE TEXT

p. 7. The Historical Setting

DUE to the notorious Thomas Warburton, East London has an unhappy association with the ill-treatment of the mentally sick. He owned a number of licensed madhouses (privately owned houses licensed for the reception of the mentally sick for profit) in the East End of London at the beginning of the nineteenth century. The White House received pauper patients from other boroughs of London and also private patients. In 1810 more than 100 patients died of typhus, yet in 1815 there were still some 300 patients incarcerated in this house. Warburton nevertheless evaded the censure of the Select Committee of 1815, set up to inquire into the abuses practised in private madhouses, but at the second inquiry in 1827 he was severely reprimanded and forced to improve the conditions in his infamous houses. It is hard to believe that the enlightened members of the committee permitted him to retain a licence.

In fact a licence continued to be granted to the owners of the White House long after Thomas Warburton's death, though under conditions which were a vast improvement on the horrific methods of incarceration practised under Warburton. The furore over the conditions in Warburton's madhouses led finally to the reforms embodied in the 1828 Act, and also in the ultimate development of the County Lunatic Asylums to protect people from falling into the clutches of the private madhouse owners. 'If the White House is to be taken as a fair specimen of similar establishments your committee cannot too strongly or too anxiously express their conviction that the greatest possible benefit will accrue to pauper patients by the erection of a County Lunatic Asylum.'[1]

[1] H.C.J. 19th Feb. 1928 quoted by Jones, K., *Lunacy, Law and Conscience*, p. 141.

171

Thereafter East London mental patients went to one or other of the London County Asylums until the 1946 National Health Service Act brought the mental hospitals under the Ministry of Health, and catchment areas were reorganized under regional hospital boards. However, long after 1828, impoverished mentally sick folk from this area also continued to be admitted to the workhouses as 'pauper lunatics'; even today senile patients from the borough are sometimes admitted to the near-by Old People's Home housed in what was the local workhouse, and yet other senile patients are living on National Assistance either in Reception Centres or Part III Accommodation. The ghosts of the Poor Law are not yet laid.

By the mid-nineteenth century it was generally accepted (in spite of the humane system instituted by Tuke and the enlightened reforms at Hanwell) that the mentally sick should be segregated from the community in large isolated asylums, hidden from the gaze of the curious and the insensitive by high walls. These were originally built to prevent the barbaric habits of the previous century when mental patients were sometimes offered as public entertainment. Unfortunately, they soon served as an unnecessary form of security and as a means of helping the public to forget the mentally sick, or to think of them as something terrifying, shrouded in mystery and better locked up out of sight.

The Act of 1845 set up a system of inspection and notification which was consolidated in the Act of 1890 which added the safeguard of insisting upon the presence of a Justice of the Peace as a defender of civil liberty in every case of certification. The mental deficiency legislation of 1913 centralized authority in the Board of Control and thereby strengthened the regulations for inspection. 1920 marked the severing of East London's connexion with the private mental hospital in the White House, for in this year Dr. Wills, the last holder of the licence, removed the hospital to the West Country, and the White House and surrounding estate became the property of the local borough council, the house itself being converted into the public library. The open space in front of the library is still referred to locally as 'the barmy Park' though few people recognize the origin of the name. The next Act of major significance was passed in 1930 and marked the first beginnings of a new era in mental health for it introduced the possibility of voluntary or temporary admission to mental hospitals.

The foundation for the integration and unification of Mental Health Services was then laid in the National Health Service Act of 1946, which swept away the remnants of the Poor Law and put mental health services theoretically on an equal footing with other health services; (in practice they are still by no means equal and the cost allowed per patient in a mental hospital is still less than in other hospitals, and the difference in grants to the blind and grants to the mentally sick outside of hospital can be as much as £5 a week, to name only two discrepancies). This integration was to be further established by the Mental Health Act of 1959, but the patients co-operating in this survey came to hospital in 1956 and 1957 and therefore were not affected by this Act. Their time in hospital, however, covered a turning point in mental hospital history, for during this period the Royal Commission, appointed in 1954 to examine the laws relating to mental illness and mental deficiency, considered the evidence and made their report, which, in turn, formed the basis of the 1959 Act.

The survey patients therefore came to hospital at a time when mounting dissatisfaction with the regulations concerning the care of the mentally sick had culminated in the appointment of the Commission.

p. 14. Admission to hospital under the new Act

Since the Mental Health Act, 1959, came into force the majority of patients enter Long Grove hospital as informal patients, just as they would enter a general hospital, without formality of any kind. Others are admitted on a compulsory treatment order for which the signature of the psychiatrist and one other doctor (not a magistrate) is needed.

Patients may still be sent to an observation unit by a general practitioner calling in the Mental Welfare Officer. If it is necessary for the patient to remain in hospital when the observation order expires, and the patient refuses to seek informal admission, then the nearest relative is contacted by the Mental Welfare Officer and an application for treatment is placed before a doctor (when possible the patient's own practitioner) and a psychiatrist of the hospital where the sick person is a patient. Certain psychiatrists are recognized for this purpose as 'responsible officers'. The psychiatrist and another doctor may then issue a treatment order. A treatment order can be enforced for a period of one year, but application to extend this must be made after ten months. The order restricts the patient's departure from hospital.

If the nearest relative objects to the application for a treatment order then the doctor and Mental Welfare Officer must bring the matter to court to obtain a decision as to whether the relative's objection is reasonable.

If it becomes necessary to issue a treatment order for a person who is already either an informal patient or under observation in Long Grove Hospital, the Epsom Mental Welfare Officer will contact the relative in East London, either directly or through the L.C.C. Mental Welfare Officer, and will call an Epsom general practitioner to the hospital to sign the order with the Long Grove psychiatrist. Appeals can be made to the Mental Health Review Tribunal at six-monthly intervals.

Special provisions are made in the Act for the long-term supervision of psychopaths. These provisions apply to patients diagnosed solely as psychopathic. At the end of 1960 no patient had been received at Long Grove to whom these provisions could apply; the diagnosis of psychopathy being linked with that of other mental illness in all cases.

p. 22. *Activation of childhood trauma*

In his article Dr. Listwan describes a number of immigrant patients who developed paranoid reactions triggered off by acute stresses during their experiences as refugees. 'The tendency to react with neurotic symptoms rooted in childhood is activated by recent hardships and the conditioned responses are reformulated. Serious social factors revive infantile conflicts.' He points out that, 'The delusions are localized and never bizarre. They frequently do not incapacitate the patients and allow them to continue their work. Particularly in primitive personalities they are frequently coloured by a mono-symptomatic bodily complaint, particularly of a sexual nature.'

In the five instances referred to in the text the patients had all been in a state of stress for some time due to deaths in the family or changed circumstances. They each managed to continue their everyday lives, but broke down almost immediately after the burglary. Each of these patients had very specific delusions and three managed to continue working in spite of these delusions. Four of the patients complained of a physical symptom: two of the women continually referred to pains and abnormalities in their bowels; a third complained of the effects of attempted rape (a delusion), while the fourth patient, a man, had spasms which severely affected his breathing.

p. 27. The reorganization of mental health work in the L.C.C.

November 1st, 1960, was the duly appointed day for the 1959 Mental Health Act to come into force. On that day the L.C.C. reallocated the work of its D.A.O.s, community P.S.W.s and organizers for work with the mentally defective on a divisional basis. A principal Mental Welfare Officer and one of the senior Mental Welfare Officers remain at County Hall. The number of Mental Welfare Officers has been increased to 32. These are working in the nine L.C.C. divisions with the welfare staff and organizers from the former departments for the supervision of the mentally defective. The five community P.S.W.s have been allocated to divisions. However, the staff for evening and night duty remains at two and for day-time duty at week-ends at three.

Note: p. 80. Marriage and mental illness

Evidence supporting these suggestions can be found in both Peter Marris's study of widowhood and Peter Townsend's study of old people.

' "It's my boy that keeps me going, I don't know where I'd be without him. . . . If I'm lonely I wait for him to come in. . . . He tries to take his father's place. . . ." But if young children are brought up to take their father's place and acquire so early a sense of responsibility towards their mother, it may sometimes be difficult for them to reconcile their adult role at home with their child's role at school. The premature burden may cramp their development and they may never feel free to marry and make a life of their own.'[1]

'The evidence suggests that widows' children often delayed marriage, sometimes indefinitely. This appears to be one of the ways by which a family adjusts to the loss of one of its members and compensates the individual who is most affected. The children, to some extent at least, substituted for their fathers.'[2]

[1] Marris, P., *Widows and their Families*, pp. 66–67.
[2] Townsend, P., op. cit., p. 81.

Many isolated pieces of evidence concerning marriage, widowhood and divorce in relation to mental illness have been gathered; similarly the effects of these latter two events on the mental health of the children of such marriages have also been studied. But it seems unlikely that the total pattern of relationships between marriage selection, marriage breakdown and mental illness will be understood until the evidence is collected for both marriage partners over at least three generations of marriage.

Widowhood may be caused by age-gaps between the parents and may in turn lead to an age-gap between the children of widows and the children's spouses (because the child who remains at home with a widowed parent delays marriage and the chance of obtaining a partner of similar age is then very limited). Research has shown (U.S.A., Public Health Department) that children of parents of disparate age have chances of physical ill-health proportionate to the age-gap. The wider the gap in age between the parents the more likely the child will be to have ill-health or physical disability. This experiment has not been repeated for mental health.

Widows themselves and divorced persons are found in mental hospitals more frequently (almost twice as often) than would be expected from their distribution in the general population. But single people are even more likely to be admitted to mental hospital than widows and the divorced. Ødegård[1] concluded that marriage 'selected' the normal members of society, but obviously between the one extreme of the normal who marry the normal, and the other extreme of the mentally sick who never marry, there is a group which is made up of the widowed, divorced and separated, many of whom are mentally ill. While it is often taken for granted that mental disturbance leads to broken marriage, and that the children of such marriages may themselves make unsatisfactory marriages, it is rarely suggested that mental illness leads to widowhood and that this also may be a self-perpetuating pattern. Yet the choice of an a-typical marriage partner due to some emotional instability or mental imbalance, especially if it is associated with a wide age-gap between spouses, might easily lead to this.

On the basis of the figures collected by them, Abel-Smith and

---

[1] Ødegård, Ø., 'New Data on Marriage and Mental Disease: The incidence of Psychoses in the Widowed and Divorced'.

Titmuss[1] suggested, 'Marriage and its survival into old-age would seem to be a powerful safeguard against admission to hospitals in general and to "chronic" and mental hospitals in particular.' But Ødegård in his study of a mental hospital population decided that while 'selection by marriage' was a probable explanation of the high rate of single people in hospital 'protection by marriage' was not, because many widows were psychotic before widowhood and only a few could be said to develop mental sickness as a direct result of the loss of a marriage partner. Ødegård's study showed that the divorced and single had the highest admission rates to mental hospital, followed by widows and next by remarried widows, while the married had the lowest admission rates. He felt that the lower rate for remarried widows added confirmation to the theory of selection by marriage.

The examination of the marriage patterns of the small number of widows in this sample suggests that among the total widowed population there is a group of people who at the time of their marriage already have certain elements in their lives which make it extremely likely that they will be widowed and mentally ill later in life. There is perhaps an argument for 'selection by widowhood'.

p. 102. *Mental patients' re-employment*

Under the 1940 Disabled Persons Registration Regulations it was suggested that the D.R.O. in the hospital area should interview those patients who wished to see him and who were about to be discharged from the hospital. Their employment is discussed and details of their requirements passed on to the D.R.O. in the home area to which the patient is returning. This scheme has now been extended and help is also given by the D.R.O. at the Epsom Exchange in finding work for patients in the hospital area while they are still living in the hospital.

p. 137. *Attitudes to the unfortunate*

Some widows, due to their sensitivity and fear of being objects of charity or pity, adopted a somewhat hostile attitude towards those who offered help. At the same time if they persisted in remaining withdrawn in their grief this inevitably cut them off

---

[1] Abel-Smith, B., and Titmuss, R. M., op. cit., p. 145.

from others eventually. Some of the wives of mentally sick men found themselves in a very similar position.

p. 152. *Experimental schemes*

Apart from the Retreat at York which occupies its own special position in the history of mental hospitals, many other hospitals have evolved new methods of hospital administration, therapeutic communities, rehabilitation schemes, and have introduced new forms of work for the patient. These developments have mainly taken place since the last war.

The following list names only a few of the hospitals which have introduced experimental schemes of their own:

Banstead	Creighton Royal	Melrose
Belmont	De La Pole	Netherne
Bristol	Goodmayes	Powick
The Cassel	The Ingrebourne	Warlingham Park
Cheadle Royal	Centre	

APPENDIX 4

LIST OF REFERENCES

ABEL-SMITH, BRIAN and TITMUSS, R. M. *The Cost of the National Health Service in England and Wales.* Cambridge University Press. 1956.

CUMMING, ELAINE and JOHN. *Closed Ranks.* An experiment in Mental Health Education. Harvard University Press. 1957.

FORSYTH, GORDON and LOGAN, ROBERT F. L. *The Demand for Medical Care.* Published for the Nuffield Provincial Hospitals Trust, by the Oxford University Press. 1960.

MALZBERG, B. and LEE, E. S. *Migration and Mental Disease.* Social Science Research Council (U.S.A.). 1956.

MARRIS, PETER. *Widows and their Families.* London, Routledge and Kegan Paul. 1958.

TOWNSEND, PETER. *The Family Life of Old People.* London, Routledge and Kegan Paul. 1957.

YOUNG, M. and WILLMOTT, P. *Family and Kinship in East London.* London, Routledge and Kegan Paul. 1957.

ZILBOORG, G. *A History of Medical Psychiatry.* New York, W. W. Norton and Co. Inc. 1941.

Articles and Reports to which reference has been made

BLIGH, E. C. Preface to *Handbook for Relieving Officers.* London County Council.

BROOKE, E. M. 'Mental Health and the Population'. *Eugenics Review.* Jan. 1960. 51.4.

BROWN, G. 'Social Factors influencing length of hospital stay of schizophrenic patients'. *British Medical Journal.* 12th Dec. 1959.

CARSTAIRS, G. M., *et al.* 'Occupational Treatment of Chronic Psychotics'. *Lancet.* 12th Nov. 1955.

CARSE, J., *et al.* 'A District Mental Health Service'. *Lancet.* 4th Jan. 1958.

CLAUSEN, JOHN A. and YARROW, MARIAN RADKE. 'Paths to the Mental Hospital.' *Journal of Social Issues.* Vol. XI. No. 4. 1955.

List of References

GALLOWAY, J. F. 'Integration of Preventive and Curative Health Services through Comprehensive Local Administrative Units'. *Lancet*. 2nd July 1960.

GOFFMAN, E. 'On the Characteristics of Total Institutions'. *Symposium on Preventive and Social Psychiatry*. Govt. Printing Office. Washington 1958.

LEIGH, DENIS. 'Schizophrenia in General Practice'. *The Practitioner*. June 1960.

LISTWAN, I. 'Mental Disorders in Migrants'. *World Mental Health Quarterly Journal*. Nov. 1959.

LOGAN, W. P. D. and CUSHION, A. A. 'Morbidity Statistics from general practice'. Vol. 1. General Register Office. *Studies in Medical and Population Subjects, No. 14*. London H.M.S.O. 1958.

MACMILLAN, DUNCAN. 'Mental Health Services of Nottingham'. *International Journal of Social Psychiatry*. Vol. IV. No. 1. 1958.

MONRO, A. B. 'A concept of Mental Health obtained by Comparing a Normal and a Disordered Population'. *International Journal of Social Psychiatry*. Spring 1956.

MONRO, A. B. 'Behaviour Patterns in Mental Disorder'. *Journal of Mental Science*. Vol. 102. No. 429. Oct. 1950.

ØDEGÅRD, ØRNULV. 'New Data on Marriage and Mental Disease. The incidence of Psychoses in the Widowed and Divorced'. *Journal of Mental Science*. 99. 417. Oct. 1953.

Registrar General's Statistical Review of England and Wales 1950–51. *Supplement on General Morbidity, Cancer and Mental Health*. London, H.M.S.O. 1955.

Registrar General's Statistical Review of England and Wales 1954–56. *Supplement on Mental Health*. London, H.M.S.O. 1960.

Census, 1951, England and Wales. County Report, London. London, H.M.S.O. 1953.

Report of the County Medical Officer of Health. London County Council. 1957.

Report of the Royal Commission on the Law Relating to Mental Illnesses and Mental Deficiency. London, H.M.S.O. 1957.

INDEX

Index

Mental patients, (continued)
 diagnosis of, 6, Appendix II
 going out to work, 8
 housing, 112–118
 marital status of, 5
 National Insurance and, 112
 new status of, 14, 29
 number of, 1
 number interviewed, 4
 number of difficult, to interview, 5
 proportion of old people among, 6, Appendix II
 reaction to, 42, 51–56
 spontaneous groups, 152–154
Monro, A. B., 151–152
Mother,
 care of several sick children, 69
 -daughter tie, 38, 76
 death of, 66, 71, 78, 170
 perception of sons behaviour, 47
 possessiveness, 71
 relation with schizophrenic sons, 67, 68, 70
 separation from, 77, 78
 special attention from, 67
 still living, 67, 77
 widowed, 75, 80

National Assistance, 107–112
 and the senile, 110
 lack of knowledge of, 111
 living on, 91, 92
 objection to, 92, 111
 officers attitude to patients, 108, 109
 percentage of patients dealt with by, 108
 travel grants from, 38
Neighbours
 attitude of, 48, 70
 intervention of, 58, 87
 relations with, 21–23, 85, 137
Nottingham, 63, 147, 148

Observation Unit, 24, 25
Ødegård, Ø, 79, 175–177
Orphanage, 44

Police
 relations with, 21, 25–27, 87
Poverty, 74, 90–96, 109, 153
Psychiatric Social Workers, 125–128
Psychotic
 admitted from East London, 146
 attitude to, 147
 'born', 40
 help for, 142, 144, 145
 'made', 41
 retained in hospital, 146

Rehabilitation, 100, 157
Relatives,
 attitude to bureaucracy, 148
 attitude to illness, 46
 and voluntary bodies, 150
 care by, 73, 82
 effect of loss of, 66
 -in-law, 47–48, 72
 keeping sick out of hospital, 88
 lack of, 78, 79
 living near, 74
 number interviewed, 4
 problems of, 2
 reaction to hospital, 32, 58, 59
 request for patients admission, 19, 88
Responsibility, 29, 49, 59, 60, 62, 63
 relief from, 80
 to other relatives, 75
Royal Commission, 2, 173

Sample
 classification of, 168–169
 numbers in, 4
 selection of, 3–4
Senility, 21
 admission of, 31
 attitude to, 108
 proportion of certified, 22
Settlements, 112, 140–142, 149
Single, the, 35, 36, 66–74, 165–166, 169–170
 high proportion among patients, 64, 65, 66
 leaving rather than entering borough, 74
 receiving help, 96

183

The International Library of

Sociology

and Social Reconstruction

Edited by **W. J. H. SPROTT**
Founded by **KARL MANNHEIM**

ROUTLEDGE & KEGAN PAUL
BROADWAY HOUSE, CARTER LANE, LONDON, E.C.4

CONTENTS

PRINTED IN GREAT BRITAIN BY HEADLEY BROTHERS LTD
109 KINGSWAY LONDON WC2 AND ASHFORD KENT

GENERAL SOCIOLOGY

Gibson, Quentin. The Logic of Social Enquiry. *240 pp. 1960. 24s.*

Goldschmidt, Professor Walter. Understanding Human Society. *272 pp. 1959. 21s.*

Johnson, Harry M. Sociology: a Systematic Introduction. *Foreword by Robert K. Merton. 710 pp. 1961. (2nd Impression 1962.) 42s.*

Mannheim, Karl. Essays on Sociology and Social Psychology. *Edited by Paul Keckskemeti. With Editorial Note by Adolph Lowe. 344 pp. 1953. 30s.*
Systematic Sociology: An Introduction to the Study of Society. *Edited by J. S. Erös and Professor W. A. C. Stewart. 220 pp. 1957. (2nd Impression 1959.) 24s.*

Martindale, Don. The Nature and Types of Sociological Theory. *292 pp. 1961. 35s.*

Maus, Heinz. A Short History of Sociology. *234 pp. 1962. 28s.*

Myrdal, Gunnar. Value in Social Theory: A Collection of Essays on Methodology. *Edited by Paul Streeten. 332 pp. 1958. (2nd Impression 1962.) 32s.*

Ogburn, William F., and **Nimkoff, Meyer F.** A Handbook of Sociology. *Preface by Karl Mannheim. 612 pp. 46 figures. 38 tables. 4th edition (revised) 1960. 35s.*

Parsons, Talcott and **Smelser, Neil J.** Economy and Society: A Study in the Integration of Economic and Social Theory. *362 pp. 1956. (2nd Impression 1957.) 35s.*

Rex, John. Key Problems of Sociological Theory. *220 pp. 1961. 25s.*

FOREIGN CLASSICS OF SOCIOLOGY

Durkheim, Emile. Suicide. A Study in Sociology. *Edited and with an Introduction by George Simpson. 404 pp. 1952. 30s.*
Socialism and Saint-Simon. *Edited with an Introduction by Alvin W. Gouldner. Translated by Charlotte Sattler from the edition originally edited with an Introduction by Marcel Mauss. 286 pp. 1959. 28s.*
Professional Ethics and Civic Morals. *Translated by Cornelia Brookfield. 288 pp. 1957. 30s.*

Gerth, H. H., and **Wright Mills, C.** From Max Weber: Essays in Sociology. *502 pp. 1948. (4th Impression 1961.) 32s.*

Tönnies, Ferdinand. Community and Association. *(Gemeinschaft und Gesellschaft.) Translated and Supplemented by Charles P. Loomis. Foreword by Pitirim A. Sorokin. 334 pp. 1955. 25s.*

SOCIAL STRUCTURE

Andrzejewski, Stanislaw. Military Organization and Society. *With a Foreword by Professor A. R. Radcliffe-Brown. 226 pp. 1 folder. 1954. 21s.*

Cole, G. D. H. Studies in Class Structure. *220 pp. 1955. (2nd Impression 1961.) 21s.*

Coontz, Sydney H. Population Theories and the Economic Interpretation. *202 pp. 1957. (2nd Impression 1961.) 25s.*

Coser, Lewis. The Functions of Social Conflict. *204 pp. 1956. 18s.*

Eisenstadt, S. N. From Generation to Generation: Age Groups and Social Structure. *374 pp. 1956. 42s.*

Kelsall, R. K. Higher Civil Servants in Britain: From 1870 to the Present Day. *268 pp. 31 tables. 1955. 25s.*

Marsh, David C. The Changing Social Structure of England and Wales, 1871-1951. *296 pp. 63 tables. 1958. 28s.*

SOCIOLOGY AND POLITICS

Barbu, Zevedei. Democracy and Dictatorship: Their Psychology and Patterns of Life. *300 pp. 1956. 28s.*

Benney, Mark, Gray, A. P., and Pear, R. H. How People Vote: a Study of Electoral Behaviour in Greenwich. *Foreword by Professor W. A. Robson. 256 pp. 70 tables. 1956. 25s.*

Bramstedt, Dr. E. K. Dictatorship and Political Police: The Technique of Control by Fear. *286 pp. 1945. 20s.*

Crick, Bernard. The American Science of Politics: Its Origins and Conditions. *284 pp. 1959. 28s.*

Hertz, Frederick. Nationality in History and Politics: A Psychology and Sociology of National Sentiment and Nationalism. *440 pp. 1944. (4th Impression 1957.) 32s.*

Kornhauser, William. The Politics of Mass Society. *272 pp. 20 tables. 1960. 25s.*

Laidler, Harry W. Social-Economic Movements: An Historical and Comparative Survey of Socialism, Communism, Co-operation, Utopianism; and other Systems of Reform and Reconstruction. *864 pp. 16 plates. 1 figure. 1949. (3rd Impression 1960.) 50s.*

Mannheim, Karl. Freedom, Power and Democratic Planning. *Edited by Hans Gerth and Ernest K. Bramstedt. 424 pp. 1951. 35s.*

Myrdal, Gunnar. The Political Element in the Development of Economic Theory. *Translated from the German by Paul Streeten. 282 pp. 1953. (3rd Impression 1961.) 25s.*

Polanyi, Michael, F.R.S. The Logic of Liberty: Reflections and Rejoinders. *228 pp. 1951. 18s.*

Verney, Douglas V. The Analysis of Political Systems. *264 pp. 1959. (2nd Impression 1961.) 28s.*

FOREIGN AFFAIRS: THEIR SOCIAL, POLITICAL AND ECONOMIC FOUNDATIONS

Bonné, Alfred. The Economic Development of the Middle East: An Outline of Planned Reconstruction after the War. *192 pp. 58 tables. 1945. (3rd Impression 1953.) 16s.*

State and Economics in the Middle East: A Society in Transition. *482 pp. 2nd (revised) edition 1955. (2nd Impression 1960.) 40s.*

Studies in Economic Development: with special reference to Conditions in the Under-developed Areas of Western Asia and India. *322 pp. 84 tables. (2nd edition 1960.) 32s.*

Douglas, Dorothy W. Transitional Economic Systems. The Polish-Czech Example. *384 pp. 1953. 25s.*

Hughes, Everett C. French Canada in Transition. *252 pp. 49 tables. 16 figures. 4 maps. 1946. 16s.*

Mayer, J. P. Political Thought in France from the Revolution to the Fifth Republic. *164 pp. 3rd edition (revised) 1961. 16s.*

Schenk, H. G. The Aftermath of the Napoleonic Wars: The Concert of Europe—an Experiment. *250 pp. 17 plates. 1947. 18s.*

Schlesinger, Rudolf. Central European Democracy and its Background: Economic and Political Group Organization. *432 pp. 1953. 30s.*

Thomson, David, Meyer, E., and Briggs, A. Patterns of Peacemaking. *408 pp. 1945. 25s.*

Trouton, Ruth. Peasant Renaissance in Yugoslavia, 1900-1950: A Study of the Development of Yugoslav Peasant Society as affected by Education. *370 pp. 1 map. 1952. 28s.*

SOCIOLOGY OF LAW

Gurvitch, Dr. Georges. Sociology of Law. *With a Preface by Professor Roscoe Pound. 280 pp. 1947. (2nd Impression 1953.) 24s.*

Renner, Karl. The Institutions of Private Law and Their Social Functions. *Edited, with an Introduction and Notes by O. Kahn-Freund. Translated by Agnes Schwarzschild. 336 pp. 1949. 28s.*

CRIMINOLOGY

Cloward, Richard A., and Ohlin, Lloyd E. Delinquency and Opportunity: A Theory of Delinquent Gangs. *248 pp. 1961. 25s.*

Friedländer, Dr. Kate. The Psycho-Analytical Approach to Juvenile Delinquency: Theory, Case Studies, Treatment. *320 pp. 1947. (5th Impression 1961.) 25s.*

Glueck, Sheldon and Eleanor. Family Environment and Delinquency. *With the statistical assistance of Rose W. Kneznek. 340 pp. 1962. 35s.*

Grygier, Tadeusz. Oppression: a Study in Social and Criminal Psychology. *Foreword by Hermann Mannheim. 392 pp. 1954. 28s.*

Mannheim, Hermann. Group Problems in Crime and Punishment, and other Studies in Criminology and Criminal Law. *336 pp. 1955. 28s.*

Morris, Terence. The Criminal Area: A Study in Social Ecology. *Foreword by Hermann Mannheim. 232 pp. 25 tables. 4 maps. 1957. 25s.*

Spencer, John C. Crime and the Services. *Foreword by Hermann Mannheim. 336 pp. 1954. 28s.*

Trasler, Gordon. The Explanation of Criminality. *144 pp. 1962. 20s.*

SOCIAL PSYCHOLOGY

Barbu, Zevedei. Problems of Historical Psychology. *248 pp. 1960. 25s.*

Blackburn, Julian. Psychology and the Social Pattern. *184 pp. 1945. (6th Impression 1961.) 16s.*
The Framework of Human Behaviour. *182 pp. 1947. (2nd Impression 1953.) 15s.*

Fleming, C. M. Adolescence: Its Social Psychology: With an Introduction to recent findings from the fields of Anthropology, Physiology, Medicine, Psychometrics and Sociometry. *288 pp. (2nd edition 1962.) 18s.*
The Social Psychology of Education: An Introduction and Guide to Its Study. *136 pp. (2nd edition (revised) 1959.) 11s.*

Fleming, C. M. (Ed.). Studies in the Social Psychology of Adolescence. *Contributions by J. E. Richardson, J. F. Forrester, J. K. Shukla and P. J. Higginbotham. Foreword by the editor. 292 pp. 29 figures. 13 tables. 5 folder tables. 1951. 23s.*

Halmos, Paul. Solitude and Privacy: a Study of Social Isolation, its Causes and Therapy. *With a Foreword by Professor T. H. Marshall. 216 pp. 1952. 21s.*
Towards a Measure of Man: The Frontiers of Normal Adjustment. *276 pp. 1957. 28s.*

Hollitscher, Walter. Sigmund Freud: An Introduction. A Presentation of his Theory, and a Discussion of the Relationship between Psycho-Analysis and Sociology. *140 pp. 1947. (2nd Impression 1950.) 12s.*

Homans, George C. The Human Group. *Foreword by Bernard DeVoto. Introduction by Robert K. Merton. 526 pp. 1951. (3rd Impression 1959.) 28s.*
Social Behaviour: its Elementary Forms. *416 pp. 1961. 30s.*

Klein, Josephine. The Study of Groups. *226 pp. 31 figures. 5 tables. 1956. (3rd Impression 1962.) 21s.*

Linton, Ralph. The Cultural Background of Personality. *132 pp. 1947. (4th Impression 1958.) 16s.*
See also Yang, M.

6

Mayo, Elton. The Social Problems of an Industrial Civilization. With an appendix on the Political Problem. *180 pp. 1949. (4th Impression 1961.) 15s.*

Ridder, J. C. de. The Personality of the Urban African in South Africa. A Thematic Apperception Test Study. *196 pp. 12 plates. 1961. 25s.*

Rose, Arnold M. (Ed.). Mental Health and Mental Disorder: A Sociological Approach. *Chapters by 46 contributors. 654 pp. 1956. 40s.*
Human Behavior and Social Processes: an Interactionist Approach. *Contributions by Arnold M. Ross, Ralph H. Turner, Anselm Strauss, Everett C. Hughes, E. Franklin Frazier, Howard S. Becker, et al. 696 pp. 1962. 56s.*

Spinley, Dr. B. M. The Deprived and the Privileged: Personality Development in English Society. *232 pp. 1953. 20s.*

Wolfenstein, Martha. Disaster: A Psychological Essay. *264 pp. 1957. 23s.*

Young, Professor Kimball. Personality and Problems of Adjustment. *742 pp. 12 figures. 9 tables. 2nd edition (revised) 1952. (2nd Impression 1959.) 40s.*
Handbook of Social Psychology. *658 pp. 16 figures. 10 tables. 2nd edition (revised) 1957. (2nd Impression 1960.) 35s.*

SOCIOLOGY OF THE FAMILY

Banks, J. A. Prosperity and Parenthood: A Study of Family Planning among the Victorian Middle Classes. *262 pp. 1954. 24s.*

Chapman, Dennis. The Home and Social Status. *336 pp. 8 plates. 3 figures. 117 tables. 1955. 35s.*

Folsom, Joseph K. The Family and Democratic Society. *With chapters in collaboration with Marion Bassett. 782 pp. 1948. 35s.*

Klein, Viola. The Feminine Character: History of an Ideology. *With a Foreword by Karl Mannheim. 256 pp. 1946. 16s.*

Myrdal, Alva and **Klein, Viola.** Women's Two Roles: Home and Work. *238 pp. 27 tables. 1956. 25s.*

Parsons, Talcott and **Bales, Robert F.** Family: Socialization and Interaction Process. *In collaboration with James Olds, Morris Zelditch and Philip E. Slater. 456 pp. 50 figures and tables. 1956. 35s.*

THE SOCIAL SERVICES

Ashdown, Margaret and **Brown, S. Clement.** Social Service and Mental Health: An Essay on Psychiatric Social Workers. *280 pp. 1953. 21s.*

Hall, M. Penelope. The Social Services of Modern England. *416 pp. 5th edition (revised) 1960. 28s.*

Heywood, Jean S. Children in Care: the Development of the Service for the Deprived Child. *256 pp. 1959. 25s.*

Jones, Kathleen. Lunacy, Law and Conscience, 1744-1845: the Social History of the Care of the Insane. *268 pp. 1955. 25s.*
Mental Health and Social Policy, 1845-1959. *264 pp. 1960. 28s.*

Jones, Kathleen and Sidebotham, Roy. Mental Hospitals at Work. *220 pp. 1962. 30s.*

Kastell, Jean. Casework in Child Care. *Foreword by M. Brooke Willis. 320 pp. 1962.*

Rooff, Madeline. Voluntary Societies and Social Policy. *350 pp. 15 tables. 1957. 35s.*

Shenfield, B. E. Social Policies for Old Age: A Review of Social Provision for Old Age in Great Britain. *260 pp. 39 tables. 1957. 25s.*

Trasler, Gordon. In Place of Parents: A Study in Foster Care. *272 pp. 1960. 25s.*

Young, A. F., and Ashton, E. T. British Social Work in the Nineteenth Century. *288 pp. 1956. 25s.*

SOCIOLOGY OF EDUCATION

Banks, Olive. Parity and Prestige in English Secondary Education: a Study in Educational Sociology. *272 pp. 1955. 25s.*

Collier, K. G. The Social Purposes of Education: Personal and Social Values in Education. *268 pp. 1959. (2nd Impression 1962.) 21s.*

Connell, W. F. The Educational Thought and Influence of Matthew Arnold. *With an Introduction by Sir Fred Clarke. 332 pp. 1950. 23s.*

Cumming, Ian. Helvetius: His Life and Place in the History of Educational Thought. *With an Introduction by Nicholas Hans. 288 pp. Frontispiece. 1 folder. 1955. 25s.*

Dale, R. R. From School to University: A Study with special reference to University Entrance. *288 pp. 23 tables. 1954. 21s.*

Evans, K. M. Sociometry and Education. *158 pp. 1962. 18s.*

Gasset, José Ortega y. Mission of the University. *Translated with an Introduction by Howard Lee Nostrand. 104 pp. 1946. (2nd Impression 1952.) 12s. 6d.*

Hans, Nicholas. New Trends in Education in the Eighteenth Century. *278 pp. 19 tables. 1951. 25s.*
Comparative Education: A Study of Educational Factors and Traditions. *360 pp. 3rd (revised) edition 1958. (2nd Impression 1961.) 23s.*

Jacks, M. L. Total Education: A Plea for Synthesis. *184 pp. 1946. (4th Impression 1955.) 16s.*

Mannheim, Karl and Stewart, W. A. C. An Introduction to the Sociology of Education. *208 pp. 1962. 21s.*

Ottaway, A. K. C. Education and Society: An Introduction to the Sociology of Education. *With an Introduction by W. O. Lester Smith. 212 pp. 1953. (4th Impression 1960.) 18s.*

Peers, Robert. Adult Education: A Comparative Study. *398 pp. 2nd edition 1959. 35s.*

Samuel, R. H., and Thomas, R. Hinton. Education and Society in Modern Germany. *212 pp. 1949. 16s.*

Wittlin, Alma S. The Museum: Its History and its Tasks in Education. *328 pp. 24 plates. 18 figures. 1949. 28s.*

SOCIOLOGY OF CULTURE

Fromm, Erich. The Fear of Freedom. *286 pp. 1942. (8th Impression 1960.) 21s.*
The Sane Society. *400 pp. 1956. (2nd Impression 1959.) 28s.*

Mannheim, Karl. Diagnosis of Our Time: Wartime Essays of a Sociologist. *208 pp. 1943. (7th Impression 1962.) 18s.*
Essays on the Sociology of Culture. *Edited by Ernst Mannheim in cooperation with Paul Kecskemeti. Editorial Note by Adolph Lowe. 280 pp. 1956. (2nd Impression 1962.) 28s.*

Weber, Alfred. Farewell to European History: or The Conquest of Nihilism. *Translated from the German by R. F. C. Hull. 224 pp. 1947. 18s.*

SOCIOLOGY OF RELIGION

Argyle, Michael. Religious Behaviour. *224 pp. 8 figures. 41 tables. 1958. 25s.*

Knight, Frank H., and Merriam, Thornton W. The Economic Order and Religion. *242 pp. 1947. 18s.*

Watt, W. Montgomery. Islam and the Integration of Society. *320 pp. 1961. (2nd Impression.) 32s.*

SOCIOLOGY OF ART AND LITERATURE

Beljame, Alexandre. Men of Letters and the English Public in the Eighteenth Century: 1660-1744, Dryden, Addison, Pope. *Edited with an Introduction and Notes by Bonamy Dobree. Translated by E. O. Lorimer. 532 pp. 1948. 32s.*

Bruford, W. H. Chekhov and His Russia: a Sociological Study. *256 pp. 1948. 18s.*

Misch, Georg. A History of Autobiography in Antiquity. *Translated by E. W. Dickes. 2 Volumes. Vol. 1, 364 pp., Vol. 2, 372 pp. 1950. 45s. the set.*

SOCIOLOGY OF KNOWLEDGE

Hodges, H. A. The Philosophy of Wilhelm Dilthey. *410 pp. 1952. 30s.*

Mannheim, Karl. Essays on the Sociology of Knowledge. *Edited by Paul Kecskemeti. Editorial note by Adolph Lowe. 352 pp. 1952. (2nd Impression 1959.) 35s.*

Schlesinger, Rudolf. Marx: His Time and Ours. *464 pp. 1950. (2nd Impression 1951.) 32s.*

Stark, W. The History of Economics in its Relation to Social Development. *104 pp. 1944. (4th Impression 1957.) 12s.*
America: Ideal and Reality. The United States of 1776 in Contemporary Philosophy. *136 pp. 1947. 12s.*
The Sociology of Knowledge: An Essay in Aid of a Deeper Understanding of the History of Ideas. *384 pp. 1958. (2nd Impression 1960.) 36s.*
Montesquieu: Pioneer of the Sociology of Knowledge. *244 pp. 1960. 25s.*

URBAN SOCIOLOGY

Anderson, Nels. The Urban Community: A World Perspective. *532 pp. 1960. 35s.*

Ashworth, William. The Genesis of Modern British Town Planning: A Study in Economic and Social History of the Nineteenth and Twentieth Centuries. *288 pp. 1954. 25s.*

Cullingworth, J. B. Housing Needs and Planning Policy: A Restatement of the Problems of Housing Need and "Overspill" in England and Wales. *232 pp. 44 tables. 8 maps. 1960. 28s.*

Dickinson, Robert E. City Region and Regionalism: A Geographical Contribution to Human Ecology. *360 pp. 75 figures. 1947. (4th Impression 1960.) 25s.*
The West European City: A Geographical Interpretation. *600 pp. 129 maps. 29 plates. 2nd edition 1962. 55s.*

Dore, R. P. City Life in Japan: A Study of a Tokyo Ward. *498 pp. 8 plates. 4 figures. 24 tables. 1958. 45s.*

Glass, Ruth (Ed.). The Social Background of a Plan: A Study of Middlesbrough. *Preface by Max Lock. 298 pp. 37 tables. 21 folder maps and graphs in pocket. 1948. 42s.*

Gutkind, E. A. Revolution of Environment. *Demy 8vo. 476 pp. 32 plates. 60 figures. 3 folder maps. 1946. 32s.*

Jennings, Hilda. Societies in the Making: a Study of Development and Redevelopment within a County Borough. *Foreword by D. A. Clark. 286 pp. 1962. 32s.*

Kerr, Madeline. The People of Ship Street. *240 pp. 1958. 23s.*

Orlans, Harold. Stevenage: A Sociological Study of a New Town. *344 pp. 1 figure. 3 maps. 1952. 30s.*

RURAL SOCIOLOGY
(*Demy 8vo.*)

Bracey, H. E. English Rural Life: Village Activities, Organizations and Institutions. *302 pp. 1959. 30s.*

Infield, Henrik F. Co-operative Living in Palestine. *With a Foreword by General Sir Arthur Wauchope, G.C.B. 170 pp. 8 plates. 7 tables. 1946. 12s. 6d.*
Co-operative Communities at Work. *204 pp. 15 tables. 1947. 18s.*

Saville, John. Rural Depopulation in England and Wales, 1851-1951. *Foreword by Leonard Elmhirst. 286 pp. 6 figures. 39 tables. 1 map. 1957. 28s. (Dartington Hall Studies in Rural Sociology.)*

Williams, W. M. The Country Craftsman: A Study of Some Rural Crafts and the Rural Industries Organization in England. *248 pp. 9 figures. 1958. 25s. (Dartington Hall Studies in Rural Sociology.)*
The Sociology of an English Village: Gosforth. *272 pp. 12 figures. 13 tables. 1956. (2nd Impression 1956.) 25s.*

SOCIOLOGY OF MIGRATION
(Demy 8vo.)

Eisenstadt, S. N. The Absorption of Immigrants: a Comparative Study based mainly on the Jewish Community in Palestine and the State of Israel. *288 pp. 1954. 25s.*

Little, Dr. K. L. Negroes in Britain: A Study of Racial Relations in English Society. *320 pp. 1947. 25s.*

Richmond, Anthony H. Colour Prejudice in Britain: A Study of West Indian Workers in Liverpool, 1941-1951. *212 pp. 3 figures. 25 tables. 1954. 18s.*

SOCIOLOGY OF INDUSTRY AND DISTRIBUTION
(Demy 8vo.)

Anderson, Nels. Work and Leisure. *280 pp. 1961. 28s.*

Gouldner, Alvin W. Patterns of Industrial Bureaucracy. *298 pp. 1955. 21s.*
Wildcat Strike: A Study of an Unofficial Strike. *202 pp. 10 figures. 1955. 16s.*

Jefferys, Margot, with the assistance of Winifred Moss. Mobility in the Labour Market: Employment Changes in Battersea and Dagenham. *Preface by Barbara Wootton. 186 pp. 51 tables. 1954. 15s.*

Levy, A. B. Private Corporations and Their Control. *Two Volumes. Vol. 1, 464 pp., Vol. 2, 432 pp. 1950. 80s. the set.*

Levy, Hermann. The Shops of Britain: A Study of Retail Distribution. *268 pp. 1948. (2nd Impression 1949.) 21s.*

Liepmann, Kate. The Journey to Work: Its Significance for Industrial and Community Life. *With a Foreword by A. M. Carr-Saunders. 230 pp. 40 tables. 3 folders. 1944. (2nd Impression 1945.) 18s.*
Apprenticeship: An Enquiry into its Adequacy under Modern Conditions. *Foreword by H. D. Dickinson. 232 pp. 6 tables. 1960. (2nd Impression.) 23s.*

11

Smelser, Neil J. Social Change in the Industrial Revolution: An Application of Theory to the Lancashire Cotton Industry, 1770-1840. *468 pp. 12 figures. 14 tables. 1959. (2nd Impression 1960.) 40s.*

Williams, Gertrude. Recruitment to Skilled Trades. *240 pp. 1957. 23s.*

ANTHROPOLOGY
(Demy 8vo.)

Crook, David and Isabel. Revolution in a Chinese Village: Ten Mile Inn. *230 pp. 8 plates. 1 map. 1959. 21s.*

Dube, S. C. Indian Village, *Foreword by Morris Edward Opler. 276 pp. 4 plates. 1955. (4th Impression 1961.) 25s.*
India's Changing Villages: Human Factors in Community Development. *260 pp. 8 plates. 1 map. 1958. (2nd Impression 1960.) 25s.*

Fei, Hsiao-Tung. Peasant Life in China. *Foreword by Bronislaw Malinowski. 320 pp. 14 plates. 1939. (5th Impression 1962.) 30s.*

Fei, Hsiao-Tung and Chang, Chih-I. Earthbound China: A Study of Rural Economy in Yunnan. *Revised English edition prepared in collaboration with Paul Cooper and Margaret Park Redfield. 346 pp. 7 plates. 50 tables. 1948. 20s.*

Gulliver, P. H. The Family Herds. A Study of Two Pastoral Tribes in East Africa, The Jie and Turkana. *304 pp. 4 plates. 19 figures. 1955. 25s.*

Hogbin, Ian. Transformation Scene. The Changing Culture of a New Guinea Village. *340 pp. 22 plates. 2 maps. 1951. 30s.*

Hsu, Francis L. K. Under the Ancestors' Shadow: Chinese Culture and Personality. *346 pp. 26 figures. 1949. 21s.*
Religion, Science and Human Crises: A Study of China in Transition and its Implications for the West. *168 pp. 7 figures. 4 tables. 1952. 16s.*

Kelsen, Hans. Society and Nature: A Sociological Inquiry. *414 pp. 1946. 25s.*

Lin Yueh-Hwa. The Golden Wing: A Sociological Study of Chinese Familism. *Introduced by Raymond Firth. 264 pp. 1947. 18s.*

Lowie, Professor Robert H. Social Organization. *494 pp. 1950. (3rd Impression 1962.) 35s.*

Maunier, René. The Sociology of Colonies: An Introduction to the Study of Race Contact. *Edited and translated by E. O. Lorimer. 2 Volumes. Vol. 1, 430 pp., Vol. 2, 356 pp. 1949. 70s. the set.*

Mayer, Adrian C. Caste and Kinship in Central India: A Village and its Region. *328 pp. 16 plates. 15 figures. 16 tables. 1960. 35s.*
Peasants in the Pacific: A Study of Fiji Indian Rural Society. *232 pp. 16 plates. 10 figures. 14 tables. 1961. 35s.*

Osborne, Harold. Indians of the Andes: Aymaras and Quechuas. *292 pp. 8 plates. 2 maps. 1952. 25s.*

Smith, Raymond T. The Negro Family in British Guiana: Family Structure and Social Status in the Villages. *With a Foreword by Meyer Fortes. 314 pp. 8 plates. 1 figure. 4 maps. 1956. 28s.*

Yang, Martin C. A Chinese Village: Taitou, Shantung Province. *Foreword by Ralph Linton. Introduction by M. L. Wilson. 308 pp. 1947. 23s.*

DOCUMENTARY
(*Demy 8vo.*)

Belov, Fedor. The History of a Soviet Collective Farm. *250 pp. 1956. 21s.*

Meek, Dorothea L. (Ed.). Soviet Youth: Some Achievements and Problems. *Excerpts from the Soviet Press, translated by the editor. 280 pp. 1957. 28s.*

Schlesinger, Rudolf (Ed.). Changing Attitudes in Soviet Russia.
   1. The Family in the U.S.S.R. *Documents and Readings, with an Introduction by the editor. 434 pp. 1949. 30s.*
   2. The Nationalities Problem and Soviet Administration. Selected Readings on the Development of Soviet Nationalities Policies. *Introduced by the editor. Translated by W. W. Gottlieb. 324 pp. 1956. 30s.*

Reports
of the Institute
of Community Studies

(*Demy 8vo.*)

Jackson, Brian and **Marsden, Dennis.** Education and the Working Class: Some General Themes raised by a Study of 88 Working-class Children in a Northern Industrial City. *268 pp. 2 folders. 1962. 28s.*

Marris, Peter. Widows and their Families. *Foreword by Dr. John Bowlby. 184 pp. 18 tables. Statistical Summary. 1958. 18s.*
Family and Social Change in an African City. A Study of Rehousing in Lagos. *196 pp. 1 map. 4 plates. 53 tables. 1961. 25s.*

Mills, Enid. Living with Mental Illness: a Study in East London. *Foreword by Morris Carstairs. 196 pp. 1962. 28s.*

Townsend, Peter. The Family Life of Old People: An Inquiry in East London. *Foreword by J. H. Sheldon. 300 pp. 3 figures. 63 tables. 1957. (2nd Impression 1961.) 30s.*

Willmott, Peter and **Young, Michael.** Family and Class in a London Suburb. *202 pp. 47 tables. 1960. (2nd Impression 1961.) 21s.*

Young, Michael and **Willmott, Peter.** Family and Kinship in East London. *Foreword by Richard M. Titmuss. 252 pp. 39 tables. 1957.*

The British Journal of Sociology. *Edited by D. G. MacRae. Vol. 1, No. 1, March 1950 and Quarterly. Roy. 8vo., £2 12s. 6d. a number, post free. (Vols. 1-10, £3 each.)*

All prices are net and subject to alteration without notice